Carthaginian
for a Day

Previous Work by H. B. Sargent

DISCOVERIES OF HISTORY

But the nations became wrathful, and your own
wrath came, and the appointed time for the dead to
be judged, and to give (their) reward to your slaves
the prophets and to the holy ones and to those fearing your name, the small and the great, and to bring
to ruin those ruining the earth.

> —Revelation 11:18
> New World Translation of the
> Holy Scriptures

It is no great wonder if in long process of time, while
fortune takes her course hither and thither, numerous coincidences should spontaneously occur. If the
number of variety of subjects to be wrought upon
be infinite, it is all the more easy for fortune, with
such an abundance of material, to effect this similarity of results. #

> —Plutarch
> THE PARALLEL LIVES
> Sertorius, Page 678

> # History repeats itself.
> —Proverb

There are striking parallels in history which only
point up the fact that we must learn from history if
we are to avoid repeating the mistakes of history.

> —H. B. S.

IV

Carthaginian for a Day

An Historical Romance
By H. B. Sargent

With An Introduction
By Cecilia Collett

SARGENT COLLETT

CARTHAGE

105741

Published in 1981 by SARGENT COLLETT
Suite 1042 N, 485 Fifth Avenue, New York, N. Y. 10017

Library of Congress Catalog Card Number: 81-90291
Printed in the U. S. A. by Enquire Printing and Publishing Co., Inc.
601 West 54th Street, New York, N.Y. 10019

To R. J. S.

Acknowledgements

To the late Elizabeth Thurman for her encouragement and enthusiasm regarding this work and to her friend the editor for innovative suggestions, especially respecting the beginning of the story. Also, to W. H. B., III for his letter of March 4, 1965—the seminal event to lead to CARTHAGINIAN FOR A DAY.

Foreword

The story to follow was written, in its original form, around the time of the emergence of détente in Soviet-West relations.

Now, the Free World should not be deceived by this new twist of co-existence, a mere slogan suddenly become an obeah of Soviet Union good will, sparking at once the demise of The Cold War and the instauration of now at long last *true* co-existence— a climate barely to exist even in the last days of the tzars. 1

Were the invasions of Hungary (1956), Czechoslovakia (1968), and now the virtual annexation of Afghanistan supposed to represent détente's credo "live and let live?" Her professions of being a peace-loving nation remain just diaphanous enough to persuade one the leopard has not yet changed its spots.

The basics of this work, similarly, were completed in the period when Lyndon B. Johnson was exalting his thesis about *The Great Society*. It is not strange the doctrine evoked little interest in the Soviet Union. For her abiding concern, as always, has been *The Great Soviet Empire*. And what is the aim of this empire? It is simply to achieve world hegemony. 2

This remains the ultimate goal, even allowing for a tired ideology or geopolitics in a narrower sense as the role of expediency might decree.

But the actuation functions basically through a process of unrelenting concentric buffer-zone expansion, radiating out with the Kremlin, at the very heart of Muscovy, serving as the innermost fortress.

Such metastasis is an endemic sociopolitical response to the innumerable invasions Russia herself has experienced throughout her history.

Like the Roman Empire of yore (whose catalyst was the sacking of Rome by the Gauls in 390 B.C.) Russia has adhered to a pattern of defensive expansion through all the stages of her history 3—

from the distant days of the year 862 in Novgorod when the three Varangian brothers Ruric, Sineus and Truvor got it all started.

One final comment about this work.

With accent on the ethnocentric, scholars maintain that the name "Greek" is but a Roman sobriquet for "Hellene," that the inhabitants of ancient Greece styled themselves "Hellenes," not "Greeks"—which designation they regarded as a demeaning Roman invention (similarly preferring "Hellenic" to "Grecian").

In a like manner, the Carthaginians very probably did not deign to label their contests with the Romans "Punic Wars"—preferring a more idoneous term, such as "Roman" or "Italian Wars." For that reason, in concert with the prevailing habitudes, "Punic Wars" where used appears in italics.

H.B.S.

The Layout of Nations

IN THE YEAR 218 B.C.—Western Mediterranean world entirely:

Rome, Carthage, Syracuse—*and* Utica—beyond the Frontier Age (i.e., the Great Western Mediterranean Frontier Age (c. 1600—c. 225 B.C.))

IN THE YEAR 1965 A.D.—the industrial West and the communist world only:

The Free World (led by the United States and chief allies), the Soviet Union, mainland China—*and* France—beyond the Frontier Age (i.e., the Great European Frontier Age (c. 1350—c. 1910))

(Rome likened to the Russian empire
Carthaginian empire likened to the Free World
Syracuse likened to mainland China
Utica likened to France)

(Russian penetration of Eastern Europe, as an outcome of World War II, likened to Roman annexation of Punic Sicily at the close of the first *Punic War*
Russian expansion in the East in the Nineteenth century at the expense of China likened to Roman domination of Syracuse early in the First *Punic War*)

("The Tall One," the domineering statesman of Utica, likened to Charles de Gaulle of France
The plans of Sanhedrinist Hanno for a "great Carthaginian Society" likened to Lyndon B. Johnson's The Great Society
The allusion *external barbarians* employed in the Great Sanhedrin deliberations likened to the Romans, with the Russians their chief counterpart today

Utica's jealousy, attended by openly spying on Carthage for Rome, likened to French envy leading to such permissiveness as to convert their intelligence respecting the United States into a vehicle ultimately to serve the Soviet Union's K.G.B.)

H.B.S.

FOUR CITIES

CARTHAGE   Founded 850 or 814 or c. 822 B.C. by Phoenicians (according to legend, Tyrian expatriates under Dido) (completely demolished by Scipio Africanus Minor in 146 B.C.)

SYRACUSE   Founded 743 B.C. by Corinthian colonists (forced into an alliance with Rome in 262 B.C.; final surrender to Rome in 212 B.C. after a prolonged siege)

ROME   Founded 753 B.C. (according to the most insistent legend, by Romulus)

UTICA   Founded c. 1100 B.C. by Phoenicians (probably traders from Tyre) (became an uncertain ally of Rome; Scipio Africanus Major captured the town in 203 B.C.)

THE *PUNIC WARS*

FIRST – 264—241 B.C.
SECOND – 218—201 B.C.
THIRD – 149—146 B.C.

The Carthaginian Empire

At its zenith it embraced a part of Libya, East and West Numidia, Punic Sicily (the Western and Northern parts), the Balearic Islands and that of Malta, at least enclaves on both Sardinia and Corsica and its own city-state province in Africa. In addition, at some point Carthage absorbed both the Lipari (or Aeolian) and Aegadian Islands and those of Pantelleria, Lampedusa (largest of the Pelagic Islands) and Ustica, located north of Sicily.

With the passage of time she also annexed several of the Phoenician colonies along the African coast—viz., Hippo, Hadrumetum and the two Leptes and, probably somewhere along the line, the enigmatic Utica. By the middle of the Fifth century B.C. Carthaginian realms extended westward to the Atlantic, eastward to the Great Syrtis and southward to Lake Triton.

Carthage, in addition, was the possessor of trading posts along the coast of Spain, notably, the port of Gadir (mod. Cádiz), Málaga and Tartessus, and probably of settlements in the Canary Islands and as far down the African coast as Sierra Leone.

There were also treaties favorable to Carthage with the Romans, the Etruscans and some of the Greeks, which may have included the paying of tribute.

While master of a goodly part of Sicily, Carthage never pacified the entire island, thanks to Syracusan resistance to the encroachments. At the close of the First *Punic War* Carthage, in addition to paying an indemnity, ceded to Rome Punic Sicily, the Lipari Islands and most probably the Aegadian Islands also.

Between the first two wars, moreover, Rome surreptitiously (and hence in violation of the peace treaty) encroached on the enclaves in both Sardinia and Corsica that belonged to Carthage and probably expelled her mariners from the island of Ustica.

However, Carthage more than offset all her losses from the first *Punic War* on with the acquirement of an empire in Spain (which, of course, eventuated in the Second *Punic War)*. At its deepest penetration the Carthaginian army was at the Ebro River, which meant its soldiery had conquered almost all of what is now modern Spain.

With the advent of the Second *Punic War* Hannibal with dispatch crossed the Pyrenees and headed his elephant equipped forces for Italy—which moves considerably greatened the scope of the Carthaginian Empire for a brief time.

Until deep into the First *Punic War* Carthage, fulfilling her presumed destiny as a great seafaring city-state of the western Mediterranean, had steadfastly downplayed the routes to empire that stemmed from the amassment of territory as such. Rather, her predilection had remained to become the dominant maritime power with ultimate decision-making authority over the western Mediterranean, fending off sporadic challenges by the Greeks, led by powerful Syracuse—that is, until the insurgent Romans seriously leveled a threat to the Punic monopoly by becoming themselves a maritime nation, derived from Roman ingenuity and Greek navigational expertise.

It was this combine that finally led to the defeat of Carthage in that bloody struggle, the First *Punic War*. Like the second contest, this one too changed the course of history: at the risk of oversimplifying, the First *Punic War* witnessed the Roman espousal of naval warfare; the Second *Punic War* encompassed the decisive Battle of the Metaurus (207 B.C.); the Third *Punic War* proved absolutely nothing—save in the complete effacing of Carthage the Romans were only to ossify themselves as "bloody barbarians."

But it was under the leadership of Hamilcar Barca and members of his celebrated family, including the Great Hannibal, that Carthage, pursuant to her defeat in the First *Punic War,* fearing for her very existence persuaded herself to change the national trend by embarking on a course of land expansion.

Unfortunately, this grand departure from tradition—as is so well-recorded—was robbed of proper, well-merited fruits of fulfillment by a devastating confluence of most lamentable events. Such was the cataclysmic slate of adversity that one day was to scroll the awesome eradication of this ancient queen-city-state of Africa herself.

H.B.S.

Location and Topography of Carthage

Located on the north coast of Africa across from the western end of Sicily—according to the 11th edition of *Encyclopaedia Britannica,* "it was situated in the heart of the Sinus Uticensis (mod. Gulf of Tunis), which is protected on the west by the promontory of Apollo (mod. Ras Ali el Mekki), and on the east by the promontory of Mercury or Cape Bon (mod. Ras Addar). Its position naturally formed a sort of bastion on the inner curve of the bay between the Lake of Tunis on the south and the marshy plain of Utica (Sukhara) on the north. Cape Gamart, the Arab village of Sidi-bu-Said and the small harbour of Goletta (La Goulette, Halk el Wad) form a triangle which represents the area of Carthage at its greatest, including its extramural suburbs. Of this area the highest point is Sidi-bu-Said, which stands on a lofty cliff about 490 ft. high. On Cape Gamart (Kamart) was the chief cemetery; the citadel, Byrsa, was on the hill on which today stand the convent of Les Pères Blancs (White Fathers) and the cathedral of St. Louis. The harbours lay about three-fifths of a mile south of Byrsa, near the modern hospital of the Karam, at Cartagenna (sic). The tongue of land, which runs from the harbours as far as Goletta, to the mouth of the Catadas which connects the Lake of Tunis with the sea, was known as *taenia* (ribbon, band) or *ligula* (diminutive of *lingua,* tongue). The isthmus connecting the peninsula of Carthage with the mainland was roughly estimated by Polybius as 25 stades (about 15,000 ft.); the peninsula itself, according to Strabo, had a circumference of 360 stades (41 m.). The distance between Gamart and Goletta is about 6 m.

From Byrsa, which is only 195 ft. above the sea, there is a fine view . . . "

From "Carthage" in *Encyclopaedia Britannica,* 11th edition (1910–11).

The probable sequence of events that led up to, and launched, the Hannibalic War (the Second *Punic War*):

Hamilcar Barca, an avowed and illustrious antagonist of the far-rowing Roman empire, went to Spain in 237 B.C. There he enkindled his eleven year old son Hannibal to vow, as his famous father (and peradventure other members of the Barca tribe) had done before him, unremitting pursuit of the goal to pacify the hated Roman.

Due to the "between *Punic Wars*" successes on the Iberian Peninsula by the Carthaginians (owing to the popular and celebrated father of an ultimately *far* more celebrated son . . . until he fell in battle, and to further challenges posed by Hamilcar's son-in-law Hasdrubal (not to be confused with Hannibal's own brother) until assassinated) Rome set the Ebro River as the point of deepest penetration by Carthage into Spain and increased the indemnity to come out of the First *Punic War* settlement by 1200 talents.

The Romans then summarily crossed the Ebro River themselves (ignoring their *own* regulations) and proceeded to interfere. Hannibal, now in command, retaliated by successfully laying siege to Saguntum (219-218), a Spanish city-state "allied" with Rome.

The city on the Tiber thus, notwithstanding she was the rodomontade offender herself, declared war on Carthage in the year 218. Forthwith from there, Hannibal marched into southern Gaul, thence crossed the Alps into Italy.

In the unfolding titantic struggle to ensue it was the Roman Scipio Africanus Major who most paramountly undermined Hannibal's logistics, his efforts more than anything else auspicating the ultimate Roman triumph. 4

H. B. S.

Introduction

The work CARTHAGINIAN FOR A DAY sprang from an exchange of letters dated March and June, 1965, respectively. It is doubtless a matter of pure coincidence that the *modern* novel itself stemmed from the letter in the Eighteenth century. I hasten to add, however, this observation should not be construed as an intimation that the H. B. Sargent novel comes full circle. Those two catalytic epistles merely lifted the curtain on an historical novel. My point—a muted one—is only a wish that technology will not one day laniate altogether the letter as an art form.

As for the book CARTHAGINIAN FOR A DAY (whose take off rocket comprised the letters) there is entailed a journey into the long ago by an individual well-endowed to meet strange challenges. And, as with most visits to quaint or remote places, a raft of surprises is the rule, not the exception. Moreover, since, in this particular instance, the destination is the legendary *lost city* Carthage, the leeway for surprise is perhaps measurably greatened. Indeed, for the accumulation of unrequited curiosity across the dunes of time concerning a city that, to all intents, disappeared from the face of the earth over two millennia ago, the possibilities of gratification might almost be bewilderingly boundless.

Now, on the assumption history adumbrates at least a seeming repetitiveness, one could observe there appears a remarkable similarity between the Western Mediterranean power struggle of the Third and Second centuries B.C. and the contemporary world (embracing both Cold and Hot wars). Perhaps one might draw from the resemblances a timely lesson?

In his work DISCOVERIES OF HISTORY, a treatise on Antiquity, H. B. Sargent hypothesizes that the *Punic Wars* were not entirely a struggle for pre-eminency in the West between Rome and Carthage but a contest between Rome, Carthage, Syracuse and other Greek towns. In addition there was a minor adversary role played by Carthage's jealous rival—the African town of Utica. It seems that these ex-Phoenician colonies, Utica the older of the two, had long been in a sharp competition.

Be these matters as they may—while the great power contestation of today, featuring the protagonists the Soviet Union, com-

munist China and the Free World (a colligation of power blocks
hatched from the geopolitics of the post-World War II period), is
patently global in dimension, the *Punic Wars*—Romano-Punic-Syr-
acusan struggle—were mainly tailored to the western section of the
Mediterranean Sea. But, for the unfolding of events, both episodes
transpired in what have been irreconcilable confrontations embracing *in esse* three-sided contests.

Yet Rome and the Soviet Union illustrate land-expansion minded
powers, the one in the post-great Western Mediterranean Frontier
Age (c. 1600—c. 225 B.C.) the other in the post-great European
Frontier Age (c. 1350—c. 1910 A.D.); whereas Carthage, in similitude with the Free World pursuant to the Frontier Age and two
world wars, was primarily engaged in sea power and maritime
affairs. But the trouble has been that Rome and, two millenia thereafter, Russia built themselves navies (augmented, in the latter case,
by the development of sophisticated aeronautical and missile
power). Thus, two fateful showdowns have eventuated—the second one still this side of Armageddon.

Due to man's—demonstrated until now—incapacity to learn from
the mistakes of forebears, dooming him to repeat their errors, it
would ostensively appear a sine qua non that there must needs be
striking parallels throughout history, if only by virtue of this human
habit of repeating the mistakes of the past. Is not this but the wont
of the world?

There would seem further in evidence, highlighting an emergent
likelihood at that, that, owing to man's obliviality with respect to
learning from the experience of others, both past and present, each
generation has to learn everything at first hand all over again—
perforce fating it to discharge the task very imperfectly. After all,
man is not an intellectual per se but an emotional creature. Nonetheless, despite this mammoth constriction, he is still endowed with
a capacity to learn.

The linchpin then is how to redirect a destructive vicious cycle—
the hapless repetitive tale of history—to a provident destiny?

The Romans coined the apothegm "If you wish for peace, prepare for war." Russian policy since the end of the Second World
War scarcely runs counter to this.

It seems that the Free World proposes, but the Soviet Union
(by dint of its shackles upon myriad "peasants" and the subjugation

of unnumbered aliens, together with unstinting chicanery and *ruse de guerre* in its foreign dealings) disposes.

Her maxim—if performance is to serve as criterion—is as the arcane underpinning of her own brand of *pax Romana:* the shibboleth of a seemingly unrelenting expansion of power. This the peculiar Russian way of maintaining the peace—a ploy of the "bear hug" to pacify all and sundry protagonists. Certainly, this becomes the obverse (no matter how one is disposed to decipher it) of *pax Britannica* or *pax Americana;* and it messages the degrading of all mankind through global subversion under what the Russians would happily appellate *pax Sovietica!*

Thus, the Russians string along with Rome in their barbaric thinking—perhaps to a degree ingenuous for having become so inured, owing to the fact their brand of sense experience has been baked into the ages.

As for the mainland Chinese, from Mao Tse-tung on down the line, they are essentially, that is in ethological terms, no more advanced than that. A nation of marionettes, their rationale is plainly incommensurate with the prospects of mutual rapport either with the Soviet Union or the Free World. Like the Russian modus operandi, their kind of *pax* reduces itself to coercion and aggression—albeit an anchor to windward for both powers remains the 4,500 mile border to lie between them.

But further on the subject of comparison—there are also similarities between ancient Syracuse and mainland China—especially in their respective dealings with Rome and Russia. Syracuse had to endure a prolonged truce with the Roman, in which she was but a satellite with degrading duties to perform; while under the Manchu dynasty China was obliged to submit to four humiliating "unequal" treaties with Moscow.

Now, the letters that led to CARTHAGINIAN FOR A DAY were dispatched when Charles de Gaulle was at the apex of his power in France: because of his envy of an imaginary "Anglo-Saxon hegemony," pique at the ecumenical status of the English language, a profound mistrust (and envy) of the United States, displayed traits of character that appear pusillanimous to the point of excess for one man; his marked proclivities, for all seasons, must have simply been to try to be as unacceptably spiteful as possible—with the intent to achieve an arrogance to make him incapable of getting on with *any* human being of his day, not excluding diplomats with a thoroughly-developed ability to accommodate people.

What an unhappy turnabout for this hero of the *Free French!* Just what kind of a man was *that?* A man who stedfastly refused to cooperate with the other powers of the Free World in their struggle against the expansionist Soviet Union and mainland China (though the invasion of Czechoslovakia by Russia did leave him with second thoughts about French hostility to NATO)? Was this French potentate merely a contrary obstructionist or an outright (even if unwitting) saboteur?

In any event the Grand Charles was reported occasionally to address his wife as though he was La Belle France herself. Whatever his part on the stage of events—fool, persifleur, would-be-dictator—history would seem to fault him for incalculable mistakes. Errors of judgment of top-rank enormity: his assault on the U.S. dollar, *force de frappe* (a multi-billion dollar waste of effort), Dien Bien Phu (less than Pearl Harbor magnitude but more than the Bay of Pigs), blocking British entry into the European Common Market, his attempts to vitiate, if not scuttle, NATO, his shenanigans with the West Germans—with the astonishing aim to undermine European defense and will to sustain it—his incredibly shortsighted approach to the hoarding of gold to the disadvantage of the United States, his Donnybrook Fair performance in Canada, and, finally, his socioeconomic enterprises in France herself.

Even as so-called instigator of détente the status is an inconclusive one, since the Free World cannot be certain that it is only a neat slogan for a Trojan Horse. A tall Frenchman the late Charles de Gaulle stood, but yet a man whose accomplishments were exiguous at the last analysis. As a result, France played the part of a weak sister in the Free World alliance over much of the post-World War II period.

In the context of the broad comparison—Utica and France had similar tasks to perform. For reasons that may remain to this day unduly obscure, their function was that of irreconcilables, betrayers of the common cause and of their own heritage, or so the story seems to read.

But the falling out of peripheral parties did not alter the basic combines: Rome-Carthage-Syracuse of antiquity and Russia, China and the Free World in the present era. People may not like comparisons, in general, because they are often odious, but they still can be gloriously exciting—especially when the impact of ages is involved.

In CARTHAGINIAN FOR A DAY there seems presented at once a romantic venture into the past, amid all the fanfare of the unknown, and the churning up of historical similarities between those far back days and the contemporary hour. Since this is beyond an afternoon's exercise, what does one really make of the H. B. Sargent study? Clearly, the lock, stock and barrel investiture of a lively story with a serious comparison to emanate therefrom.

Cecilia Collett

Carthaginian
for a Day

Chapter I

Professor Andrew Hartfield drew out a handkerchief and mopped his brow as he sat at his desk. The exudation stemmed from mortification as much as the heat! Before him stacked high was a pile of unanswered correspondence. When would he ever get to it? This was Friday—but the whole weekend was all but spoken for, even though, basically, the campus had been shut down for the summer.

Mon Dieu, how things could pile up once one became embroiled in extra-curricular activities! he mused ruefully. Other people's problems, other people's activities—it was *ever* thus: they ended up high on the professor's list of priorities, even though for the great part they were none of his proper business at Lincoln State, without talking about his own personal situation—which could encompass a matrimonial venture in the immediate future.

Yet how engrossed in outside activities should a member of the faculty get? For Andrew B. Hartfield, associate professor of ancient language and classical civilization at Lincoln State General College, Worthington, Kentucky, this was the *crux criticorum* of the problem: too many duties assumed with utmost solemnity that could not truly be performed.

Normally, kenspeckle and gay (and a most eligible bachelor to boot)—he was not one practiced at letting the overall morale wilt unduly. But now he was singularly possessed by that self-deprecating mood to cavort before the mirror to see oneself as he really was. In this introspective vein he had some sobering second thoughts. Was he bogging down in certain areas . . . on a short haul basis at least . . . for undertaking too much—and, very likely, in a few areas beyond his ken? . . . even his abilities? Could his possible waywardness be due to pursuit of a career as if there were no tomorrow?

He stared listlessly at the stack of unanswered mail, then quite mechanically picked up the top piece—a card. It was from his dear friend and mentor, erstwhile teacher Jonathan T. Kent, Jr., professor of Romance languages at Atwater University, Toledo, Ohio. The card was from Sweden, where his friend was honeymooning after remarrying recently. His first wife was deceased—untimely organic complications proving fatal, and so forth.

Professor Hartfield's friend indicated that he and his bride would return to Paris in a fortnight, where the couple planned to spend the balance of the summer—at the usual Parisian address.

Given that schedule, the professor pondered, it would be malapropos to relay congratulations to the newlyweds until a week to ten days. With just an iota of relief he put the card aside.

Almost hypnotically his attention adjusted itself to the next communication of the stack: this turned out to be a letter from a godson of his—William B. Thompson III. The missive was dated March 4. *Still* unanswered, and here it was already deep into June!

With a vague persistency—as though it were already beyond the pale of legitimate acceptance—irrespective of the fact the fruits of neglect could have been compounded by debilitating heat . . . (without even endeavoring to square away in his favor the veritably massive engrossments of the young professor) . . . he scrutinized the pile of unanswered letters, with ultimate aim, perhaps, to attemper the whole process.

Then, compulsively, he returned to Billy's letter, which particularly at that point in time seared his soul.

It was the story of his life—the bustling young professor who rocketed into top-drawer eminency from this comparatively small college environment in a scant eight years since commencing his career. And he achieved this in spite of what amounted to a badge to talent and versatility, the inherent propensitude of the college to overburden the more gifted members of the faculty.

And what a frantic ten years stretch for the young professor, inclusive of a two year stint with the army—degrees to be obtained, courses to be taught, lecturing to be attended to, literary projects afoot including two books—a treatise on Sanskrit and a study on the impact of the Greek tongue—already published—and several papers already circularized; serving as a "fellow" on the campus and, as a former "spectacular" Lincoln State athlete, as assistant football and track coach. All this, together with some mounting administrative duties, and his continuing efforts with regard to oil painting rounded out an extremely active schedule.

It is always rewarding to be well-liked; Professor Hartfield was an extremely popular figure at Lincoln State, with only the most negligible degree of jealousy betrayed by his colleagues. But well-liked or not, most probably even a perspicacious young professor would, in a moment of weakness, be tempted to set great store by his own ultimate aspirations . . . with the irreducible return to earthiness at the last.

Almost out of the need to reduce to manageable size all these vocational and avocational pressures, in his immediate introverted mood of frustration . . . the somewhat overwrought professor read the letter aloud—

Professor Andrew R. Hartfield
45 Tree Lane Avenue
Worthington, Kentucky

Dear Uncle Andrew,

Please forgive the slowness with which I reply. I have always had a tendency to be delinquent in my correspondence but more so at present with an overwhelming curriculum and poor health. Besides, alacrity has never been one of my strong points. But don't take lack of celerity for lack of gratitude, for in truth I regard your paintings as one of my most treasured possessions. Your style, like a fine wine, improves with each year and becomes more distinctive. Next to the eternal, aesthetic beauty of a painting the momentary, physical pleasure derived from candy is somewhat anticlimactic but nevertheless greatly appreciated.

Speaking of food, I have lately become an experimenter in the culinary arts. This morning I completed Hemingway's *A Moveable*

Feast for the second time. In it he mentions drinking café au lait. This drink was also mentioned in *Life with Picasso* by Francoise Gilot, one of his numerous "wives."

Reading about it aroused my curiosity and taste buds, so I went to the kitchen to make some. I added equal portions of double strength instant coffee and scalding milk and added two and one half teaspoons of sugar. The results were most rewarding. I have also found that the addition of one half teaspoon of brandy enhances the flavor. I have devised what I believe to be an original recipe for coffee. I make it in the conventional method of boiled coffee, using an egg shell and a teaspoon of the white, but adding four or five cloves to the water. This gives it a unique flavor and makes the addition of cream and sugar unnecessary.

Father has kept me informed regarding your work, or should I say *studies,* embracing the languages of antiquity? I understand your tract on the Phoenician tongue, published in January, has received critical acclaim—so please accept my sincere congratulations, Uncle Andrew!

From my own position, that is a fabulous area of study—since I find it difficult just to make any headway at all . . . even in *modern* history! I just do not comprehend how you keep track of so much material—ancient language, ancient history, philosophy and the rest. Father told me recently you have a rare charism for sorting out the riddles of history! May I ask you a question, in the light of this—even though a blunt one—Uncle Andrew?

Is your obviously profound skill, in this area, due more to a knowledge of ancient languages or a broad-spectrum of historical antiquity itself? As an admiring godson I simply seek to end confusions in my own mind about my *great* Uncle Andrew.

Does possibly your extraordinary knowledge of ancient language lure you, in a manner of speaking, into the study of something else?—such as classical civilization itself? I get carried away sometimes in this respect myself. My interest in the English language leads me back to its beginnings and then I get lost. I guess my mistake is that I approach history through language. Do you, Uncle Andrew, in the course of your studies, ever approach language through history?

I think I am gradually finding myself in high school. My passions are literature, psychology, and philosophy, in that order. Whether

4

this is a harbinger of good or evil I do not yet know. I have also developed a great affinity and a minute understanding for music during the past several years. I believe I told you before about playing the Hammond Organ (spinet). If worse comes to worst I suppose I could manage to eke out a living playing professionally in restaurants as some of my friends are doing, but that is a rather haphazard foundation to build a life upon.

Hemingway has become my god in literature and I derive great pleasure from his work. With the help of my English teacher, I have learned something of narrative structure, themes, and motifs. It was not until this year that I actually understood anything of the short story or novel, but under his instruction I have dissected books to find the hidden meanings placed there by the author. I have written papers on various motifs in the standard books required by most high school courses in American literature. My teacher is a Yale graduate, so he must know what he is talking about. I have so far (knock on wood) received straight A's in his class. Whether it is this particular teacher or a change within me I cannot be sure, but in previous years I did B work and had no special interest in the subject.

Recently I wrote a short story which received a 98 for content and a 95 for structure. My teacher wants to put it in the school yearly magazine. When I write, I always base my stories on actual experience. I find I obtain much better results than when I write on a subject in which I have had no experience. Unfortunately, I have a large reservoir of experiences, some most unpleasant.

I suppose you have heard that my parents are divorced and that my father has remarried. If not, you would have inevitably heard it sooner or later. I would appreciate hearing from you. Now that the warm weather and the summer vacation is approaching, I will have time for correspondence.

Sincerely,
William B. Thompson III

H.B.SARGENT

Chapter II

A truly excellent effort by a youngster only sixteen or seventeen, assessed the professor. He must reply at once . . . and in style to discharge the relationship properly. After all, did not he as the godfather have special responsibilities with regard to this godson, and by this token did not the boy expect a certain level of performance by this so-called "mind and muscle" godfather? Yes, he must get cracking forthwith—and with the essence of insouciance and suavity.

But what about the delay—early March to mid-June? Quite a deplumating circumstance for Mr. Godfather, to be sure! How to bypass that one? In the end, "handsome is as handsome does"— and Billy will know it. He must fall back upon some sort of *legitimate* excuse, some moral suasion—but what . . . ? Wistfully he scanned the text of the letter . . . and all of a sudden a passage seemed to arrest him unduly.

> *My interest in the English language leads me back to its beginnings and then I get lost. I guess my mistake is that I approach history through language. Do you, Uncle Andrew, in the course of your studies, ever approach language through history?*

Ever approach language through history, mumbled the seemingly atrophied young professor. Then quite unceremoniously he

7

paused, a quizzical yet predetermined expression taking hold on his face. This rising into the focus of conviction—without further fuss or feathers, he commandeered the typewriter and soon commenced typing.

Master William B.Thompson III
67 High Ridge Road
Stonington, Connecticut

My dear Billy,

Many thanks for your estimable communication of the Fourth of March—which I have read more than once with no inconsiderable amount of interest and have at hand right now.

Let me say first off, your misdoubts (in specific disciplines) as to whether the most certified route to knowledge is history through language or language through history are understandable. These are in a sense facets of the times: sometimes we overlook the paramount fact that we must initially gain a degree of mastery of the mother tongue. Once we do our thing along these lines, given our predilection or options to look at language through history or history through language, whichever, we find we have enhanced our familiarity with the subject matter adequately enough either to adopt a subjective or oblique approach to things or espouse a more objective stance. It is strange but I leap in upon ancient language only to wind up sorting out history.

But before any further allusions to the content of your most thoughful epistle may be warranted, I must at the outset apologize—in my turn—for so prolonged a delay in making note of it. And, apropos of that, the tardiness sustained is not due to reasons imagined, but does relate to imagination, nonetheless. At the risk of undue divagation I will explain my point. Even in a strife-riven age, one to put forth both turmoil and derring-do, the individual shall yet seize occasions for flights of fancy; that human instrument, the imagination, cannot be but lightly suppressed or so readily chartered by those pre-emptive pressures of reality. Artful dodger— its routes are a journey of escape from that very realness (professedly more a function of adults than children, irrespective of the time-honored and transcendent propaganda that insists fairy tales are for the latter) with an ultimate destination which has been defined as the *alter mundus*.

Now, for Francis Bacon, the Seventeenth century philosopher, this imaginary world had a most practical purpose; he conceived it as a creative "root" source for evolving an inductive construction of the fabric of science; a refreshing altered mental approach that turned the mind's eye from the tedium of the insipid scholasticism, whereat it had arrived even prior to his day, to new worlds of natural science—biology and an all-embracing cosmology. In this task he doubtless prepared the way for the hypothetico-deductive process 5 that eventuated in modern science. Others, more conventional and endowed with lesser intellect, simply let their undisciplined imagination take wing and lose itself in this undefined void—one which, according to Shakespeare, houses dark powers of nature that are as the procreator of all that man creates through artifice. Whence, a delusory sphere not lodged in the mind so much as accessible to it for exploitation.

Thus, for some the production elicited from that "creative nothingness" is at a level of the fairy tale. This the harvest when the organic effort fails to bear the more generic type of romance or fiction. Of course, *all* created works must be wrought and countenanced by the peculiar mental function in question—not to say, with the same holding for the far more vast output of inarticulate and gibberish-like notions the imagination churns up from moment to moment in the course of the hours of wakefulness (finding its counterpart in the disorganized thinking to enswathe much of objective life). 6

In considering the phenomenon, I eschew the intuitive (inclusive of clairvoyance as it concerns the extra-sensory) alike dreams, visions and the realms of the subconscious—which may be considered as out of court. Similarly, I must excise altogether the curious fact that psychologists of the past century (Freud, Jung and so on) in charting human behavior, have placed too much stress on the "libido" and too little on the "ego," or if you must, "id" (veering too far afield—Freud in particular—from the basic tenets of Schopenhauer and Fichte)—since there is intended here no full-blown treatise of *penetralia mentis!* 7

Still another kind of flight of fancy—to be defined indubitably as that of the "day dream" sort—is to let the imagination adventure upon the past—mayhap a sentimental journey to some distant point in history, such as a random projecting back two millennia in time—and, with the tool of scrutiny so attuned, for one to look about him most imaginatively.

In this way, I have been literally carried away over recent weeks by the allure of past eons, out upon sundry pilgrimages ensearching the ancient—a propensitude to which I, as occasion may arise, am so wont to succumb. During such spells of gestation with the by-gone I rise to the surface of the present historical maelstrom only infrequently, somewhat the way a sleek dolphin might reascend after each game of hide and seek with a shark.

To be certain, I do not deny my bouts with antiquity embody much cry and little wool, but I do have diverting confabs, now and again, with our great-great-grand-progenitors. On my current sur-facing (having tarried a time at Seleucia on the Tigris, thence to the ancient site of Troy, where I reconstructed the saga of the son of Anchises and Aphrodite as far as the outpost Carthage—at which point my abreaction fastened upon local history, which I traced to the *Punic Wars)* I, forthwith, appropriated typewriter and set about dispatching this overdue acknowledgement.

So the Mediterranean world of classic times—fades back into the shades of obfuscity—as the pounding on my key-board con-traption resounds amid the welkin uproar, in this paramount assay to recapture the warp and woof of the living epoch . . .

In limine, let it be observed I did not in the least overlook your reference to "overwhelming curriculum and poor health." I sin-cerely hope the latter is not a serious condition, nor one so much as to hamper your aims with respect to what sounds like a very ambitious (and most probably highly commendable) regimen of scholastic and extra-curricular activities—one that you will want to continue, in some degree, even in the vacation interlude of sum-mer.

But manifestly (on the criterion of your divulgences) you are cognizant of the precise challenges to confront you in your scholastic endeavors. Even an assured sedulousness, so emphatically contrastive to the fruits of indolence, must needs produce a crop whose degree of bountifulness will go in inverse measure with inanition and the demands of health. Thus, what is called for spells not nostrum—but individual judgment.

To gain a propitious adjustment is no facile matter—but at the last analysis is not every compromise exacting enough? ". . . this is not a business," Churchill wrote, on the importance of public men cultivating a hobby, "that can be undertaken in a day or swiftly improvised by a mere command of the will."

Perhaps in no other age has man been so put to his shifts when attempting to broaden his pursuits by setting his face against the hazard of overly narrowed existence—a state to which all wage earners tend to be carried by the undertow of livelihood's exaction. The versatile student today runs a tilt at this challenge—albeit only by fits and starts. For he also (in addition to broad scholastic commitments, so often in the forefront of campus and communal responsibilities) disdains the monosyllabic life—an aspiration, upon fulfillment, so sure to befit tomorrow's leader.

Tenacity, fortitude and unwavering diligence are some of the qualities to be marshalled here: they hold, a posteriori, as much for acquiring versatility as achieving prudent work output. Without them, as with the incidence of lassitude, the endeavors are fated to be counter-productive. But I hasten to add—you seem not without this *force majeure,* as these very qualities clearly you display in abundance. Yet disengaging all this, there is still no substitute for enthusiasm—which trait, above all, you manifest in profusion!

So, congratulations—for this is your *sauce piquante,* without which the dish will be but medial.

It is quite beyond dispute that, within predetermined limits, the broader the rationale of living the more the youthful citizen should be able to accomplish in the course of his subsquent career, but the limitations imposed by one's constitution must be judiciously revered, lest health itself place the goals in jeopardy. An irrevisable rule of universality dictates that even the most precocious student must scud under bare poles, for if wanting of challenges how might he duly extend himself? Nor should one cultivate, ritualistically, an affinity for styles of living that are well-nigh wholly at variance with conventional procedures; in succinct terms originality enough but tempered in the crucibles of moderation. Like inertia itself the espousal of habits to excess becomes an additive that ultimately reduces achievement.

To recapitulate—an active schedule, one to compose courses of study (inclusive of the supervenient lateral work entailed) in combine with outside activities where practical, is one much to be desired. However, it must lose, *à toute outrance,* its import should it not be tailored to corporeal verve and health. In addition to the purely physical there are analogous requirements of morale—so much of which spring from not just spiritual concern but bodily dictates as well. Thus, for the student physical well-being and mental outlook, one and indivisible, must remain the overriding abraxas in the matter, as they enjoin the pace to be followed and the scope of the projects to be embarked upon. Indeed, I wish you every success in arriving at a suitable regimen!

Your predilection for literature, psychology and philosophy—and music—is ipso facto an impressive, well-selected choice of preferences. Your literary bents, which you expatiated upon at length, and current overall performance comprise—perforce—an enviable record; in fact, you seem to be fashioning much to affirm the encomium of attainment—in these literary efforts of yours, especially! Few young scholars betake themselves to the laying of so soundly based a foundation. And, as for the skill of writing, few citizens ever acquire it—particularly in realms beyond journalism. Both reading and writing are indispensable to the learning of this craft. At later stages formal reading can for some, with impunity, be partly replaced by research and investigatory work.

But you seem to be gathering the roses of both reading and writing. My sincere kudos to you for raising, *sous tous les rapports,* so sterling a house of scholarship and skill! You are learning early in life that one can obtain an education without becoming a gerund grinder, a hack, a narrow technician or a propagandist.

Thank you for the tidings about your father. This was the first I had heard about them—howbeit, receiving a confirmation from your father at a later date. Thank you again for your kind letter and my very best to you, your mother and members of your family.

But *satis verborum!* . . . my relapse—it seems—had not quite expended itself . . . as I slip back into history . . . and reacquire my . . . Carthaginian train of thought. . . 1920

1860

1665

1345

845

120

. . . 218 B.C.

Chapter III

(The Carthaginian Council of the Elders: Eleventh Intercalation—
Tyrian Cynosure per annum 628, old time Phoenicia 1504—Annus
Magnus—*the year 218 B.C.*)

GREAT SANHEDRIN

Magistrate Mago **8** walks hurriedly into the temple hall; bearing
a scroll, he has two fatigued, dust-laden and overheated couriers
in tow.

Mago.	(Mounting the dais he unrolls the papyrus.) Fellow countrymen—we have calamitous tidings to report! As a result of Hannibal's storming of Saguntum, Rome has declared war on Carthage! **9**
	(The sensational news transports the sanhedrin to the throes of clamorous arena—as magistrate and elder surge ensemble around Mago and the scroll! The presiding officials struggle to restore order through the council room. The din of expostulations subsides at last, and the chief magistrates of the temple conduct a colloquy, with intent to arrive at a consensus as to what course of action Carthage might take.)
Timoleon.	The high priests foretold as much! They revealed that Melkarth burst flames the other day at dawn, signi-

fying warfare and sacrifices in store. An ill-omen, indeed! More sacrificial offerings will now be mandated. When and where will we see such appetite sated?

Hamilcar. To exorcise Melkarth may be essential, my dear Timoleon, but equally wise would be some effort to conciliate Baal and his Paphian bride. 10

Himilco. The *fertility* gods, Hamilcar? Then another appetite is our concern: the need to stimulate procreation itself!

Hamilcar. One to be in the arena, for certain—but not to the exclusion of all else. (thoughtfully) We have heard it said, now that we address ourselves to the subject, the Roman seeks to refine all manner of traditional fertility rites. They say the Saturnalia pales even our most liberal holidays!

Ethball. (amused) Doubtless, it is the only way they may keep their legions in battle array. Their baggage trains do not want for captive women—but not nearly enough to administer to the men to the point of satiety. After all, my dear colleagues, are not the Romans a people of Fescennine ways!
(A wave of amusement pervades the hall.)

Himilco. I have heard it said that even the Ambarvalia has been Romanly debased. But each to his own: thus, when in Rome we cannot expect a Roman to do as a Carthaginian. How could this possibly come to pass when their very golden rule is to gainsay the privileges of civilized restraint?
(A resumption of mirth ensues among the distinguished company.)

Timoleon. As Himlico declares it in a trice, our adversaries may rest assured of one thing. The sanctuaries of Baalim will not be defiled by Romanesque homage to Baalpeor! Unlike the City of the Seven Hills, Carthage believes in public morality.
(These remarks evoke general applause.)

Hanno.   (expression of disbelief) All of this talk of fertility and Corybantic antics alters not one thing soever! Fellow citizens, have we forgot—even as we commence our deliberations—that it is war . . . war with these power-drunk aggressors across the sea? Is it not then as plain as Numidian women this wild Hannibalic venture might only end in another Roman war? How long have I been counseling that Carthage not embroil herself in Spain?

Himilco.   For far too long—you may be certain of that, colleague Hanno!

Mago.   It would appear these Romans do not concern themselves with our Numidian females, preferring to commingle with the Amazonian breed; at least they are professedly that Martian-minded!

Timoleon.   Fellow countrymen, in the light of these unhappy tidings from Rome, I submit we dispatch couriers to Syracuse. We must win over to our side every potential ally!

Ethball   Let us send couriers to Utica as well. No stone must be left unturned.

Mago.   An exercise in futility, my dear Ethball. Under the iron grip of *the tall one* Utica will elect to support the Roman all the way.

Ethball.   Simply because we have been the greater people, we cannot count on them in our extremity. What a pusillanimous leader our African neighbors have!

Hanno.   One of the prime reasons I have sought to discourage this Spanish campaign. We cannot depend on our allies!

Hasdrubal. It would seem we have had experience enough with our Utican neighbors to know them for what they are—time-servers! They will await evidence as to how go the tides of war. Then, like the good opportunists or vultures that they are they will make their choice. Lest we forget, we must ask ourselves—did

	they coalesce with us so much as a single galley in the last war, even though caused by the flagrant Roman aggression in Sicily?
Timoleon.	Surely the intelligence reports confirm that since our loss of Sicilian domains, the magistrates of Utica have been in league with Rome?
Mago	A most apt observation—could the documents recently intercepted on their courier tell otherwise? Did they not plainly establish the fact that their chief magistrate—*the tall one*—has been too freely communicating with both Roman consuls—backing their imperialism in both the West and the East?
Himilco.	*The tall one,* indeed! A magistrate who would as lief pay tribute to Rome or Syracuse and insure slavery as work with us in mutual independence.
Hamilcar.	The only pertinency, no doubt, is that once a clear and unmistakable weakness is evidenced on our part, even our provinces will prepare to secede—East Numidia, West Numidia—even our island possessions! With easiest alacrity they will all hold league with the enemy, once Utica foregoes her position in North Africa.
Timoleon.	That is the situation to a fault. Rome is not the only tribal people with whom we have to contend! In fact, we cannot even rely on our mercenaries. Have we all forgot their revolt after the Italian War **11**—wherein our beloved city herself was besieged?
Hanno.	Just another reason why our city-state is unsuited for a Spanish campaign. We simply do not have the manpower. (waxing satirical) Or should I borrow from worthy colleague Himilco . . . and call it the fertility prowess of the Romans?
Himilco.	The dilemma is not to be gaged by numbers of human beings but in terms of competing cultural centers. This fine point of distinction must be taken into account—if there is any hope for Carthage to resolve

her differences with the enemy without resorting to the battlefield.

Hamilcar. Assuredly in any provident solution of our troubles to be arrived at, there must take root in *both* camps a spirit to alleviate enmity—if war devastation is not to be the mutual legacy.

Hanno. And what profit it Carthage this Hannibalic victory of Saguntum if it only means another Italian War?

Himilco. In my opinion, our victory at Saguntum was just a pretext by the enemy to declare war—one of his so-called allies losing its seat of government. But has not Spain long been a Carthaginian sphere of influence, thanks to Hamilcar Barca and to Hasdrubal, founder of Cartagena 12, and, as an important flank, is it not vital to our maritime existence? But what, Hanno, of Roman encroachments on the islands of Sardinia and Corsica—in direct violation of the very terms of settlement of the last war—in which these barbarians virtually ended our hegemony in Sicily?

Hasdrubal. (approvingly) Himilco speaks well! The menace of these external barbarians cannot so easily be thrown into the shade. We must never again forget they do not honor their treaties—whether drawn up in the West or the East.

Ethball. As surely as we have eyes with which to see! Already Roman legions have penetrated our island system of defense. We may be secure in the Balearic Islands, but not so in the Tyrrhenian Sea—and what of Malta 13—to say nothing of the snatching of the Sicilian isle from under our very nose!

H.B.SARGENT

Chapter IV

Hamilcar.	Spain is the present answer to vulnerability, our whole Western position being at stake. My dear colleagues, do not underestimate the role of influence on human minds. This is dramatized *because* Sicily is untenable—short of open confrontation with the enemy. If war is the irrevocable course, we need a new base against Rome—one to permit us to carry the conflict to the enemy; Spain meets that requirement. We trust Hannibal will take fullest advantage of his victory— and not be intimidated by the threats of a twain of Roman consuls! (A burst of applause reverberates through the hall.)
Mago.	Eloquent notions, my dear colleague—but we forget that we are a seafaring nation, not a land empire!
Timoleon.	And, to carry that point a step further, Rome is a power whose reliance is upon land-based militarism— whereas ours reposes in maritime affairs. We must resist enemy expansion into merchant and naval areas. But we must resign ourselves to letting him subjugate the mainland.
Himilco.	(frowning) This could be very dangerous counsel!

Mago.   We must keep in mind, worthy friends, that the prevailing terrain of Spain and much of the Gallic regions beyond is mountainous. Accordingly, in such areas the advantage of our cavalry will be neutralized.

Timoleon.   A single Roman maniple could rout our elephants in those mountain passes. 14

Hanno.   (superciliously) Perchance, Hannibal is only looking for a Pyrrhic victory! Fellow countrymen, we submit our urgent business is Sicily and Rome's continuing desideratum regarding it—not Spain—not any quarter of the northern shore of the Mediterranean Sea. To war with Rome over Spain is disaster personified!

Hasdrubal.   Any business with Sicily is to invite the confrontation Hamilcar just spoke of. My dear Hanno, we dispute not the importance of Sicily. It is—I am persuaded—nothing more nor less than the prime bone of contention to divide our two imperial cities. Proximity of the Roman eagle to our shores is as an automatic cloture of debate on the matter. We must keep our defenses constantly on the alert regarding this key island. Nonetheless, could Carthage tolerate so much as six legions of Romans in Spain? My worthy colleagues, by virtue of the links to the southernmost regions—which means our back yard—such development could be sheer disaster!

Hanno.   (scornfully) Any more disastrous than having Romans in Palermo—in Lilybaeum! What is this, dear Hasdrubal, but our *front* yard?

Ethball.   (with undisguised contempt) *Senatus populusque Romanus*! That is how they style themselves abroad, but we of Carthage are not fooled by polite words—above all when they translate into plunder, rapine and rape wherever these bandits go!

Hanno.   Fellow countrymen, do not these eloquent words by Ethball settle the question once and for all? No support for further Hannibalic adventures—as once we

become overextended we will have the little monsters
at the very gates of Carthage!

Hamilcar. (impatiently) With no choice in the matter we find
ourselves engaged in another "Romano-Punic" struggle. In consequence, we must not idly wait for the
enemy to prepare our ruin; we must strike first. The
more reason, my dear Hanno, for the Spanish campaign, not to mention a European-based counterattack. Any threat to Spain is a threat to our Mediterranean position—and, as friend Himilco intimates so
well, a threat to our maritime life-line.

Ethball. Which means a threat to our very existence!

Mago. All of which returns us to the basic contradiction.
Colleague Hamilcar, as you so studiously observe, it
is our *maritime existence* that must play the predominant role. This is confirmed by our tradition and history. Therefore, we have no business concerning ourselves with the amassing of territory when not related
to our basic defensives. This is precisely what Hannibal and brother, and father before them, **15** have
been about; far from being content to set up the seaport Cartagena—the *favor of Baal* has now captured
Saguntum! In short, the danger lies not so much to
our maritime position as in becoming entrapped in a
land-based conflict with Rome!

Timoleon. And, good colleagues, the risk is enhanced threefold
for the entry of Rome into the realms of seapower.
Have we forgot the loss of our fleet off the Aegates? **16**

Hasdrubal. (yielding to sarcasm) It seems it is for the Carthaginians to propose and the Romans to dispose! Are not
their flagrant aggressions ample proof we must adopt
a hard tack against them? Is not this the only argument
to hold any validity?

Hanno. On the contrary, Hasdrubal, the only valid arguments
are those that take into account the irrefutable fact
that any war with Rome will greatly dilute our resources when our proper business should be to con-

serve them, that we might press on with the building of a great Carthaginian society . . .

Himilco. (disingenuously) Ah, what an intriguing thought—to build the great society without interference from the Romans!

Hanno. (ignoring the remark) Have we not pressing matters at home to engage our energies? Are there not canals and bridges to build; amphitheatres and baths to erect; and numerous other public domiciles to construct? Our engineers are talking of the feasibility of aqueducts—who knows, but if we concentrate on the problem, one day we may even be able to pipe water into the average home! Even as I speak, we have roads to lay out and agricultural projects to put through—to say nothing of improving relations with the provinces and expanding Carthaginian trade. (looking coldly at Himilco) These are the deeds for a great society that should take precedence over any insane adventures abroad!

Mago. In my view, this is the only rational position to assume in the circumstances.

Himilco. On the presumed assumption, my dear Mago, that we make the single exception that business comes before pleasure?

Mago. (frowning) What means Himilco by these words? Does he insinuate that in the planning of works of construction we are of a bent to disport in pleasure?

Himilco. Are not these notions of social improvement something of a pleasure in the face of war? Or is the predication Carthage will sue for peace even before the first sword strikes shield?

Ethball. My dear Himilco, they simply mean Carthaginian craftsmen will have pleasure spinning make-believe temples of Baal-zebub when not out silencing the Romans.

Hanno. (infuriated) One day silence will befall your tongue—unless you cease these desecrations and insults, colleague Ethball!

Hasdrubal. (determined to keep the debate objective) Your item-ization of projects for Carthage is a praiseworthy one, friend Hanno, but the climate is not wholly propitious for them when one makes note of the encroachments of the external barbarians upon the very island spheres whence the increased trade and resources for home improvements must come. The main threats being the collision in the Western Mediterranean, symbolized by Saguntum, and, above all, the very possibly critical penetration of the Carthaginian empire by this Roman conquest of Sicily.

Chapter V

Himilco.	The crisis has been only accentuated for the conduct of our Utican neighbors. As a result of this, we must go it alone—since there can be no help to us with *the tall one* in command!
Hasdrubal.	Outright hindrance would more aptly define his sort of help—a magistrate who seems to be in open intrigue with Rome to exploit our Sicilian losses.
Timoleon.	*The tall one* practices the same insidious game pursued back in the days of Etruria.
Himilco.	They say, and with some justification to be certain, he is as wily as a Gaul—surely now he had an ancestor at the gates of Rome the day it was sacked! (The sounds of laughter pervade the hall.)
Ethball.	For the degree of his gall *the tall one* would laugh roundly even today over this unheralded Gallicizing of Rome by lowly provincials. Yet if we may take the long and the short of him—all Utica needs is but one more stretch of a Gaul—then even Roman festivals will come to Africa! (Mirth again diffuses the hall.)
Hasdrubal.	The sad fact remains, worthy colleagues, for all his tallness and innate talent we behold just another

statesman to be ensnared by the Roman trap of divide and conquer!

Hamilcar. Let the men of Carthage not repeat the error! Our tasks would seem, thus, twofold—to quarantine the threat posed in Sicily and render all support possible to Hannibal and the field command in their efforts to challenge the enemy on the mainland. Remember, good colleagues, when Carthaginians entered Sicily to resolve differences between Messana 17 and Syracuse, it was the Italians that so invidiously destroyed our peace-keeping work. In due course, they turned upon us without warning, changing the scene into an Italian war of conquest. In this confrontation with so formidable and treacherous a foe can we do less than place our guard upon high and be prepared for the worst?

Ethball. (in conciliatory tones) And withal ask ourselves, dear friends, where are the glorious days of Mago, the councils of our founding fathers, the heritage of our immortal guardian queen?

Himilco. My worthy compeers . . . let us vow, then, that this second Roman challenge not end with anything this side of victory for Carthage. We must heed throughout the wise counsel of Hamilcar and Hasdrubal. Firstly, we must acknowledge the dangers we confront—the spectacle of external barbarians under the aegis of Roman consuls threatening us from the West and from the East, both on land and at sea—a pincers movement, as it were—by an enemy conspiratorial, relentless—and basically comprised of tribal peoples that put in jeopardy our ancient and glorious heritage—one to hold unbroken continuity with Phoenicia, with the island bastion of Tyre, with the Greeks and Trojans, Alexander and the Hellenists—a city-state whose foundress goddess-vestal Queen Elissa 18 met her Trojan consort at the very gates of Carthage; which son of Anchises and Aphrodite went himself

28

to the site of Rome and there sought in vain to civilize the wolf-like urchins Romulus and Remus—progenitors of the present day enemies of our beloved country. My worthy colleagues, let Carthage now activate herself against these barbarians!

Hasdrubal. Reflect on this one point, dear friends: to this very date our only loss, our only reversal has been Sicily— in part due to guile by the foe. In all other quarters we have kept the adversary at bay. In all other theatres we are as strong as an elephant . . .
(This draws expostulations of approval.)

Hamilcar. And let me add but this, fellow Carthaginians: we have the cavalry, we have the commanders. Our Numidian horse are legend . . . sturdy, spirited, slender and swift. Our elephants powerful and fearless— far superior to the diminutive Eastern breed. Carthage has the traditions, skills, the valor and imagination and the resourcefulness to face up to this Roman horde and put it asunder . . . Whatsoever Italian that would prevail upon us . . . he will soon discover that it is hand for hand and foot for foot when he comes to grips with Carthaginian . . .
(Many of the elders jump to their feet—vociferate their enthusiasm.)

Hanno. (taking the floor, once order was restored) Very well, my colleagues. It is plain the majority of the elders assembled here . . . on what is now becoming a dark day for Carthage. . . .(interrupted by hissing). . . .are not content just to maintain our defensives. For them the course is overtly to prosecute a conflict with Rome—not to the exclusion of invasion of her territory, irrespective of the dire risks entailed. As a consequence, we will reconsider the course of full support for the Hannibalic armies in Spain. But—it must be stipulated—we can give no formal assurances our final position will be favorable.
(This elicits notes of protest from some elders.)

Mago.   A position even more problematic, I might add, should Hannibal elect to carry the war beyond the Iberian Peninsula!
(Disorder prevails throughout the hall and Mago himself, as the presiding magistrate, restores order.)

Timoleon. It is incumbent upon us neither to exercise a readiness to negotiate nor purpose to broaden the conflict. Our onus is rather to call a halt to what is an unprincipled Roman aggression. We should not exceed the bounds of this.

Ethball.   My dear Timoleon, in the annals of war there has never been an instance, barring ignominious retreat, of stalling the advance of a ruthless foe short of counterattack.

Himilco.   Worthy Carthaginians—if we at times gave the father Hamilcar Barca something less than undivided support—let us now atone for it by backing Hannibal the son all the way and so secure our destiny . . .

(In due course Magistrate Mago makes the sign for adjournment of the council. The chant of obeisance to Melkarth is performed. A gong's macabre notes resound through the temple—the elders file out of the meeting hall.)

Chapter VI

From my listening post between two pillars in the temple . . .

Due to the gravity of the occasion (it was my good fortune to have entered the great temple before the couriers' bombshell, for directly after that the main gates had been cordonned off) I was somewhat perturbed to find, completely at unawares, that the captain of the guard had assigned more sentinels to key posts in and around the temple halls. In a word—and to my chagrin—with sheer pandemonium radiating out of the temple into the community at large, in the wake of the Roman declaration of war intelligence— the Sanhedrin guard had been doubled! So there I was blessed with an inside track which only the more augmented my jeopardy. For the prevailing superstitions of the age I was not so fatuous as to assume any interrogation to occur might confine itself to an aimless picking and sniffing.

To be certain, I had taken precautions myself from the moment I had disembarked at the harbor of Carthage. Aided by a petty piece of bartering, more in sign language than broken-Phoenician, in which I surrendered a gold watch to a goggle-eyed fishmonger, I had acquired in return a toga-like garment, which upon donning proved small but functional, and a headdress, approximating a turban. (Due to the hot sun, it was the custom in town to protect the head.) Both white in color, the garments were sufficiently presentable. Moreover, with the help of a bit of charcoal I had swarted my complexion. This left my biggest anxiety the matter of height. Literally, I stood head and shoulders over the natives!

True enough, as a partial offsetting of the hazard of conspicuousness due to height were the matters of speed and strength. As events were to confirm, I probably could have outrun even the sprint champions of the nation—achieving this feat in despite of a touch of dyspepsia acquired from some "exotic Carthaginian dish" I had sampled in the morning.

For the moment, however, these natural advantages were of small comfort. The patent fact remained the doubling of "the palace guard" could only have a like effect on the possibility of detection and subsequent arrest. Thus, here stood I in the renowned corridors of the imperial government of Carthage, at the very moment of monumental crisis! Oddly enough, I found myself drawing up a mental list of those more popular methods of torture of antiquity— reserved *especially* for enemies of state . . . traitors, criminals, spies—*the brazen bull, the rack, the grill.* Not very inviting . . . Coincidentally, I just then chanced to register on the fact a sentinel seemed to have me under surveillance from the opposite end of the colonnaded hall. Certainly, his gaze was trained my way; and there was not the remotest smile to mitigate the sternness of his visage! But prior to this discovery, which placed in bold relief the nature of my vulnerability, I had had an opportunity to take stock of things in the course of the deliberations.

Along the colonnade of the hall of the Sanhedrin were likenesses, in bust form, of great and near-great—Hamilcar Barca (soldier, statesman and father of the *great* Hannibal, who was himself too new for the honor), Mago (the statesman and founder of Punic military power), Hanno (the explorer), Hannibal and Himilco (the heroes of Acragas), and so on. 19 At the center of the temple there showed the awesome entrance to Melkarth's 20 lethal chambers— where the grisly rites of human sacrifice were discharged. The prevailing architecture of the structure seemed an admixture of Greek (the columns) and West Asian (the arches). Although the obelisks (like the pointed towers I had descried about town) were characteristically Carthaginian, they betokened an unequivocal Oriental influence.

While I was disquieted by rising apprehension over my exposed circumstances in the temple—after all, how easily I could have been mistaken for a Roman spy—I was concerned about the language barrier and how effectively I had transliterated the deliberations of the Sanhedrists. My translation was very likely indifferent, in the extreme.

However, to palliate the language obstacle, luckily the Phoenicians had "cased" for me a workable solution with their stunning contribution to Western culture—namely, an alphabet, a copy of which I had brought along with me; just as the Greeks had taken it from there, so I had to take the Carthaginian lingo—a syncretic Canaanite business—back into the Greek to make any headway at all.

Apropos of this, there remained the very character of the Sanhedrin as a deliberating body itself. Was not this an institution of Jerusalem? Let me see . . . the Greek word for it . . . *Synedrian* seemed, as translated, to support ancient Semitic definitions, inclusive of the Phoenician governmental body "council of the elders." In short, more like a senate than a court of law or a place to conduct religious services alone.

Beyond the communication gap, not at all lessened for the lack of a public address system throughout the various temple chambers to assist the uninitiated, there was a psychological block, the matter of mental outlook—in this case my own.

Now, during my brief hours in Carthage I had already exhibited a wide range of moods, almost as many as Baal the sun-god was wont to display. For their overall tone I could scarcely asseverate that everything concerning my visit could be deemed pleasurable. Not that I was scheming to quit town before the appointed hour that evening. The sheer romance of this community I found myself incapable of resisting, which impelled me occasionally to indulge in speculative trains of thought.

The rivalry between Carthage and Syracuse (and this had commenced long before the struggle with Rome) alienated the Greek settlements, since Syracuse herself was a former Greek colony. Thus, although mayhap it would have had to go glimmering, if Carthage somehow could have formed a league with the Greek enclaves, including the city-states of southern Italy, known as *Magna Graecia*—following her rapprochement with Syracuse—they might have accomplished together the isolation of the Latins and Sabines, now denoting the Romans. If they could have achieved this, in the same way the Twelve City Etruscan civilization had been reduced, these Italic peoples might ultimately have been absorbed by the Gauls.

At that point in time, at least, notwithstanding their thrust south and sacking of Rome, the Gaulic people were not driven by ambitions to be supreme in the Western Mediterranean. (In this sense they matched the Etruscans.) This would have left a viable hegemony over the entire area to Carthage and Syracuse—and the greatness of Rome would not have been. If Carthage and Utica could have worked out their differences to the benefit of both, the latter might not have felt impelled to join forces with Rome. If the rivalry of leading Carthaginian families, pushing opposing policies of land expansion and sea power, had been less intransigent, they might have directed the community along a more provident course. If Scipio Africanus Minor had been more like Scipio Africanus Major, irrespective of Cicero's admiration for the former . . . if that old codger Marcus Porcius Cato 21 had not distilled so much hate, leading to the ultimate effacement of Carthage herself . . . well, who could remotely be certain?

Still, the cogency of the fated course Carthage was to ply in this vein of

the piquancy of the Pageant of Life 22

I found hard to fend off.

Whether or not it was an Olympic Games year, if judged by the First *Punic War* the palpable fact remained that neither Rome nor her Punic rival would honor them (i..e., in compliance with the Hellenic custom, to cease hostilities for the duration of the games).

Yet there seemed a retrospective soundness to the hypothesized desideratum that Carthage, Greek Sicily and what remained of *Magna Graecia* —one way or another should have coalesced against Rome. For eschewing such defensive enterprise, history simply unveiled the inexorable outcome.

CARTHAGINIAN FOR A DAY

In the very year of the destruction of Carthage in the Third *Punic* struggle the Roman legion was to pacify all of Greece and, simultaneously, convert Macedon into the first province of Rome.

That year, also, was to see the end of the women's Olympic Games. What did they call them? Her . . . ae . . . *Heraea*. The men's Olympiad, in contrast, fared better. It was not finally to be terminated until A.D. 394, when the East Roman Emperor Theodosius the Great chose to abolish the institution altogether, probably due to the imperial challenges he was constantly confronting in Italy.

While the Games, from their very inception, had been mainly under the tutelage of warlike Sparta, under the Roman period they were to become even more politicized.

These matters aside, Rome after achieving mastery in the West, (to all intents, with the defeat of Carthage at the close of the Second *Punic War* in 201)—while biding her time for a day of reckoning against the Gauls—next was to turn East.

Suddenly, I noticed not *one* but *two* sentinels across the hall, with their attention riveted in my direction! They seemed to be conversing with one another, going about it in martial manner. With that as my little cue I felt it high time to slip back into the recesses of the temple and withdraw altogether. Acting on this impulse, it quickly dawned on me that two Carthaginian sentinels had quite unceremoniously become one Carthaginian posse!

Well, doing what came naturally, I strode into the vaulted foyer, thence gained the great corridor at the rear of the temple. This debouched via two mammoth bronze gates into a barrel-domed arcade that, flanked by great Punic gardens, led to an enfilade of imperial buildings. I deduced these housed the other arms of government—such areas as judges' chambers, popular assembly bailiwick, quarters of the elected magistrates and facilities for the administration of commerce and empire.

I had noted with relief the inner sanctum of the temple was more sparsely guarded; and, before the guards stationed there had fully tumbled to what was transpiring, I had darted through the gates and into the arcade. From there I immediately entered one of the gardens. At that moment all I could do was thank my lucky stars for its lush verdant presence!

What wondrous gardens they were—a veritable network of pool, fountain and balustrade cast amid clusters of poplar, tulip tree and balm of Gilead; row upon row of fine-trimmed hedges, demarcating beauteous blue-green plots of grass; tier upon tier of exquisitely-terraced lawns spangled by myrtle and myrrh, olive and palm tree and by bed of exotic flowers and plants. *The Hanging Gardens of Babylon* right before my eyes!

Yet in more mundane terms what a haven for fugitive! Certainly to one in my dire straits this was like stumbling upon a long lost friend—*dernier ressort,* as it were. Blanketed into "instant" security by this infinite, most marvelously variegated cover, I set about moving further and further away from the temple. While my actions had to be covert, I sought to gain as much distance as possible in the least amount of time. Simultaneously, I tried to maintain an adequate vigil by glancing back, from moment to moment, to see if any pursuit was under way.

Pausing briefly amongst a cluster of cypresses, I once more looked back. To my dismay, in spite of a comfortable distance already realized, I could verify straightaway the arcade was now alive with guards rushing to and fro, apparently exchanging much excited jabberings as they moved. As a sort of grim affirmation of the enterprise, a swarm of turtledoves and starlings hovered chaotically over the arcade. Again, my little refrain . . . *scarpines, crucifixion, impalement* . . .

A few moments thereafter I sheltered myself amid a concatenation of bushes and ferns, which in a finely landscaped sort of way framed an idyllic pool. For utter quiescence the place was unbelievably contrastive with the unrelieved hubbub of the temple arcade.

Peering through some Acacia plants, I reassured myself that there had been no penetration of the gardens by the constabulary. Hopefully, my unceremonious departure had been precipitous enough to leave the guard confounded for quite a spell. Such a situation, understandably, I felt I must exploit at all costs—since the overriding matter of a successful getaway doubtless depended upon it.

Sequestering myself securely behind a bush within the protective area of a stand of aspen, I paused a minute or two to catch my breath. The while, in light of some earlier Carthaginian discoveries, I waxed pensive.

In a weird sort of way what a genuinely *glorious* city this was . . . this lost town of the eons: its citadel reposing so augustly on Byrsa hill. And what a gorgeous vista on the harbor and the blue, blue Mediterranean! But, alas, given my strange malaise, I had neither the time nor inclination to enjoy it. Perhaps it was not a case of dyspepsia, after all. Perhaps the time lapse had something to do with it—my abrupt entry into Greater Carthage. Or maybe the cause was a psychosomatic one, induced by an anxiety about getting out of the place in one piece!

Still and all, indigestion was indigestion. I have long maintained, in fact, that, in this peculiar realm, mental outlook depended more on "manyplies" than familiarity with—say—quatrains of Omar Khayyam. But even carrying so biased a line of reasoning from the sublime to the sub-visceral, I could not be sure as to just which catalyst (or combination thereof) it was that summoned my indisposition.

Clearly at this point I was too cohibited to blandly seize reins and trot a chariot over to abode of nearest doctor. This indeed would have been the proper mode of transportation, inasmuch as Carthage had become a highly equestrianized metropolis. I had soon discovered that even at the drop of a headdress it was "to horse" in town!

But I refrained from making such a pilgrimage, chiefly for what might have awaited me on arrival. What sort of medicine would the good doctor have prescribed and what might have been the resulting effect on the patient? In fairness to the community in general, it had quite a reputation for getting the most forceful sorts of surgical work done—and in a hurry. Make no bones about that!

Earlier in the day, deciphering some Punic signs about town, I had learned that Carthage was long on barber-surgeon shops. Out of curiosity, I made an en passant stop at one of them—without, of course, getting "personally" ensnared!

From the very outset I was intrigued by their modus operandi. At once I could tell that at everyone's disposal—whether for tooth-pulling, limb-severing or whatever anatomical change one was in the market for—there was a sort of bared-to-the-chest muscular "pre-barber" surgeon type. Plying their trade with singleness of purpose—these men gravitated around tilted, box-like seats, seemingly well-provided with chains and fetters (no doubt to encourage the patient not to fag midway in the operation) and, for the most part, occupied from morning until night.

Perhaps the popularity mystique related to the *nature* of these imposing structures. While sitting it out one could not complain about a lack of security! In any case, they seemed to help the paying guest feel at home. Although this was a period well ahead of the development of anaesthesia, I thought it odd that there was almost no concrete indication of the practice of acupuncture in town.

This could have been compensated for by the sagacity of the surgeon himself. It was truly a standout! Devolving upon his instrumentation—it became the quiddity of his practice. Wiggling was frowned upon; any kind of grunt or cough was deemed a sort of "noise pollution." In short, willpower, no matter what, must be tested to the limit—for this was the homeopathic road to recovery, Carthaginian-style.

As far as the eye could see, for ordinary customer, there were at the ready mace, axe, whinyard, scimitar and shears; for the guest with acute complications there were reserved implements resembling a bronze yucca and yataghan.

When not in use the instruments reposed, neatly-arranged on walls. This was but a testimonial the arrival would not have to resign himself to a long wait and, in particular circumstances, might even be allowed to make his own selection of hardware.

From the word go I had refused to single myself out as one inherently of a procrastinative turn of mind, but thus far I had refrained from "making appointments" with these folks—dyspepsia or no dyspepsia—since would not their consultations be apt to leave one with the short end of the stick? Assuredly, I required no homily to convince myself Carthaginian barbers as a breed had the knowhow to get right down to the source of the difficulty, even though I remained loath to permit them to throw this particular baby out with the bath! I also was persuaded that craftsmen of such high skill—even when the challenge became *method indirect*—could rise to the occasion and get the job done, whether client happened to be a stoic looking for inspiration or not.

Beyond their services to the people of Carthage—I heard tell they administered faultlessly to other kinds of patients from the back rooms of their establishments: Numidian horse, African oxen and occasional dog, and not infrequently, a disgruntled captive or hostage. So, taking the long and the short of it, I bided discreetly with my dyspepsia—passing the buck to the next patient, sedentary posture, ecstacy and all.

In spite of my bout with discomfiture, my thoughts kept reverting to the Sanhedrin deliberations. Some of their observations had reminded me that Hanno, 23 in the aftermath of the First *Punic War,* had instigated a revolt of the mercenaries. With this as part of the tradition—a background of discord and contumacy—how might a nation address itself to a great competition when so divided? National unity seemed the first order of business were Carthage effectively to set her face against Rome in the ongoing struggle for hegemony. But what sort of place was this city-state Utica, situated some fifteen miles to the north? Surely with her Phoenician background she should deem herself a natural ally of Carthage, for the reason alone that African solidarity was so vital in the face of the challenge posed by Rome and Syracuse?

And who was that Utican magistrate the elders had labeled *the tall one*? What was the basis for his schemery to turn against his sister city-state? Perhaps, for emotional dislocation, he failed to comprehend that the enemy's aim was a time-tested one—to divide and conquer. Without so much as cultural and national—to say nothing of military—allegiance between the two African powers, Carthage's ability to wage the Western Mediterranean contest could hardly be enhanced.

CARTHAGINIAN FOR A DAY

CHAPTER VII

To my consternation: two tool-laden gardeners advanced in tandem around my side of the pool. Even though I was tolerably-well-concealed, they would almost certainly have spotted me when they drew abreast. My extremity, like it or not, called for pre-emptive measures. Squatting close to the hedge, I awaited their approach. A few moments went by—then with a leaping motion I lunged at the two men, the force of my moving body catapulting them into the pool! Instantly, I about-faced and hurtled myself over the hedge; then, scampering alongside, I betook myself to the waiting shelter of a cluster of olive trees.

In the set-to, mine had been a gut response, and thus beyond control or articulation. Although I scarcely regarded myself as an advocate of violence, even if only panoplied on the assumption my obsidional instincts were not more developed than those of my contemporaries—when matters reduced themselves to survival a genre of *necessity was the mother of invention*—perforce—seemed to grab hold: an atavistic activity into whose secrets I was practicably gainsaid penetration, it appeared to be more a feisty intransigency than overt infatuation with things brutish.

Satisfied that I had eluded the gardeners, I peeked out from my hiding place to ascertain how matters fared in the vicinity of the arcade. To my mounting alarm, I espied a concentration of sentinels gesticulating wildly and facing the garden on my side of the arcade.

Had they spotted me in my bout with the gardeners? Were they preparing for an outright search of the premises? In a matter of minutes a whole detachment of them would be inspecting each individual hedge—looking behind every bush.

Perhaps the most ominous development of all took place just then. Two trumpeters, epauletted with imposing insignia of the imperial realm, unceremoniously assumed positions by the arcade entrance and studiously blared their instruments! Surely this could only convey to the constabulary that the moment for action was now?

It was time to move on . . . that haunting refrain . . . a Roman spy . . . *excoriation, hot pincers, bed of Procrustes* . . .

Moving stealthily through the grove of olive trees, I traversed a behedged terrace and arrived in the vicinity of an alignment of hedges and cedar trees—which, tied to a balustrade of cascading water safeguarding a temporary refuge, allowed me to pause and take stock of things.

I had now progressed to the outer reaches of the garden, whose periphery was simply a serpentine wall, with sculptured likenesses of the big cat sitting atop it and intermittently spaced. This, I was convinced, I could scale without difficulty. The real danger to present itself related not to the wall but the hundred-foot gantlet that would have to be run from the last secluded area—namely, a row of dogwood trees, where I shortly took up my stance. I reasoned that in my final frantic sprint and attempt to surmount the wall, at the minimum a shower of arrows would be visited upon me! This was only ineluctable, since the constabulary had donned the appropriate weaponry. On the other hand, *surprise* was a factor going for me.

And, once over the wall, I could lose myself in the aura of confusion already gripping the town, like a sort of concert étude, in the wake of the Roman declaration. I had other benefactors, to be certain, that might abet my escape: the festival in honor of the goddess Baalat, to culminate in much revelry and wassail that very night, war or no war, and the fact bright afternoon before long would be yielding to the shadows of late day. In such an environment I should be able to slip through the city gates and reach the red-sailed ship on schedule.

If, in the circumstances, I plucked up less ardor than one might expect—"when in Carthage do as the Carthaginians do"—it was quite palpably due in part to my having to take exception in a number of behavioral areas. For one, the practice of not bathing regularly. I had come to discover at fairly close hand that the custom of bathing, even in the public baths (characteristic of the period by and large) was anything but remotely excessive in North Africa. Still, such habit of privation was doubtlessly shaped in part by lack of water itself. To bathe *and* perfume was what I had been thinking of; but, in short shrift, I got the strangest notion the average Carthaginian became satisfied once he had thoroughly perfumed himself to forego the bath! Maybe so. Then, also, on the strength of my mild gastric unpleasantness, I became vividly aware that in this town diet was an affair of pot luck. Taste buds, apparently, had little to do with it. However, there seemed to be exceptions to the rule.

Honey, for example, and some of the other food products not disturbed by environmental pollution Carthaginian-style or by a total lack of refrigeration. Olives, vegetables and fruits were at hand in plenitude, and they seemed savory and fresh. The fish market experienced a voluminous marketplace acceptance, reflecting the presence of a clearly vigorous industry. The rewards of an immediate environs remarkably fertile were at once plain for all to see. The vineyards of Carthage bordered on the fabulous, making wine pressing a major activity. Not alone was she the granary of the Carthaginian empire, but grain was one of her most proliferant items of export.

But turning to the slaughter-house department—some of the meats were tough and strong; I would estimate even prior to the time of pantry of plush "couch-of-the-villa" sampling that such food would have been hard to negotiate much of the time.

Meat of rare antelope and spices from the East were reserved pre-eminently for the patrician class. But in Carthage, in a quaint egalitarian sort of way, *every* citizen was "born to the manna," or so they called their horse meat.

They had another cadence to which I could not respond. This appertained to their "nectar of the gods"—which was really how they eulogized their fermented concoction—which impressed me out of hand as only a type of hard cider. I was much more laudatory in my responses to Carthaginian wine: by even modern standards heady stuff . . . if we disengage their dandelion wine, which matter of thing I found a few steps beyond the pale! The method of marketing provender was simplistic enough (if unsanitary, for the plethora of flies alone) to partially offset its limited keeping qualities, which was a way of life in town. This made no appreciable difference to Punic merchants—to say nothing of the plebs. It was likely the case, since in Dido's city the belief had long held on that strong food built strong bodies!

Now, that could have been where the Carthaginian potation played its most likely part. It seemed to permit one to down, with comparative impunity, such things as ox meat, fowl, pork, cereal cakes, hardtack, goat's milk, honey-impregnated sweet meat and numerous Mediterranean fishes, unsupported by one iota of refrigeration. A beverage of such potency would have functioned as a good decontaminator—even without pinpointing its towering participation in urban festival. Taking place with precise regularity, these episodic occasions, while in a major way dedicated to fertility obeisances, were always accompanied by much drinking and revelry.

The moment of decision was suddenly at hand! Peering around a bush, I was to witness an abrupt human dragnet leaping from arcade into the garden premises: operation search and destroy—or more likely capture, then . . . *flagellation, tongue removal, the stake* . . . Summoning my innermost sprint-style energies, I bounded for the wall and, aided by my height, got a grip on the top surface and commenced to shinny up. It was as I was pulling myself over it that the fusillade of arrows began. Happily, it was too little and too late; I was gone.

H·B·SARGENT

Chapter VIII

My new environs were markedly less nerve-racking—relatively deserted plazas and not very bustling city streets.

Although most of the streets of Carthage remained unpaved—just dirt and dust—the main arteries, which crossing at the center of town fanned out to almost the outer walls, were paved, like the great plazas themselves, with limestone. The Carthaginians—at least in the West—were pioneers in this sort of fabrication. 24

While limestone was the predominant rock used about town, for choice buildings some gray granite was in evidence, probably an import from the Egyptian world.

The sidewalks were composed mainly of limestone blocks. At intersections these were placed proportionately across the dirt road, permitting pedestrian to pass but giving right of way to horse and chariot.

The streets were narrow, ungainly and rubbish-ridden (irrespective of an active sanitation department, largely manned by slaves).

Children, wearing hardly anything more than loin cloth, scurried about, playing on the soil. As in the forenoon, from time to time a few would stare at me with disbelief, ostensibly awestruck by my size. Otherwise, I was basically in rapport with the environment for a surprisingly prolonged period, once with such needed celerity I had quit the imperial gardens.

My immediate concern reduced itself to a brush with a mere dog that, spotting me, proceeded to bark. It was furthest from my wish to attract attention just then. But the shadows of fading day would soon start to redound to my advantage. Cheered on by the prospects of becoming less and less conspicuous, I wended my "merry" way, bearing in mind that my *ultima Thule* was the northeast corner of the harbor.

No matter the rift with Rome, unmistakably, there was churned up this mellowing part of the afternoon a festive mood in Carthage. This I had diagnosed as an honor to mark the anniversary of an important deity, the goddess Baalat haedrat "mistress of the sanctuary," to be exact. 25 In my view of it, it was dampened only by menacing units of the constabulary, which had an ornery way of appearing with unmitigated abruptness, an eventuality that constrained me to keep my guard up at all times.

In marked contrast to my experience in the gardens, sweet peaceful musical notes now surreptitiously cajoled my ears! To the strains of cithara, the percussion notes of cymbals and the refrains of chanting priests—townspeople galore began to disembogue from their high places; and down into town they went, flushed with wine and dreams of Carthaginian supremacy, as the high priests with unction and ritualistic gesture concluded the more religious part of the festival.

Following this, there was to eventuate in the bethels and shrines about town the orgiastic culmination, as—once anon—the citizenry voiced their impassioned hello and fond farewell to Baal and related deities—alike acknowledging their pursuit of the traditional glories of Sidon26 and Hiram the Great, and of Phoenician exploration and trade, and of Carthaginian colonization and empire—for the present evanescing, due to the gathering Roman presence.

The street I was presently on, rather unceremoniously opened into what had the appearance of a great plaza, with which four imposing arteries were linked.

At the center of the square stood a massive eliptical building topped by a huge dome. The structure lying on what I calculated as the correct direction, curiosity afforded me an excuse to take a peek at the interior of so stunning an edifice. I forthwith discovered that this was nothing less than the mythical library of Carthage! What a glory forever gone.

Its centrosphere—a great vaulted hall—was apparently the main reading room. Handsome carved marble panels arrayed about the hall were presumably the repository of myriad manuscripts that the staff would furnish to readers upon request.

A modulus of carved stone tables and benches were arranged in arcs around the hall, spaced not too far from the walls. On either flank was a sizable orifice opening into wings. These were elongated, arcade-like rooms with arched ceilings.

A number of students and scholars were studying writings in the main room, while the side rooms were apparently reserved for the scribes. There quite a few of them, bowed over tables, were completely absorbed in translating onto papyri, with something quite like quill pens, cuneiform characters and other abstruse writing, along with Greek and Latin.

I soon took note that my brief survey of the premises was adequate to excite the attention of the attendants, two or three of whom wore emblems that bespoke marshal status. In consequence, I felt an immediate egression was the most discreet next move for me, having no urge to court yet another incident in, of all places, the Carthaginian library!

I shortly had crossed the square and entered the street that seemingly would betake me to the downtown area and finally the main gates.

In my decurtate observations on city life, for want of something more concrete, the predilection was to be disregardant of a number of important topics—such as, the scope and character of commerce; the degree to which money—gold and silver coin and bullion—had outmoded the practice of barter (although, to be certain, coins had long been minted and the money-changers discharged their accustomed role in the social order); manufacture of earthenware including clay lamps, plowshares, chariots, armor and weapons of all kinds and the potter's wheel; and such industries as agronomical betterment for all crops concerned, ship-building, metalworking (inclusive of silversmithing) and glass blowing.

Although Carthage trafficked in ivory, metals, precious stones and all the products of Central Africa (transported north by caravan) and pursued a vigorous commerce in slaves—and, notwithstanding her ready access to silver and gold, copper and tin, plaudits to such convenient bastions as Cartagena, her most sensational enterprise seemed to be textiles. Punic weaving, advancing the Phoenician tradition as it pertained to textiles and dyes (especially Tyrian purple), had become outstanding in its own right, and Carthaginian fabrics were celebrated throughout the Mediterranean. 27

On the institution of slavery itself, outside the province of galley slaves, I was disposed to ignore the variables of such categories of servitude as Numidian salt mines, supportive areas of agriculture, households of the elite, concubinage and departments of municipal government. While the signs of slavery were everywhere, it would be an exercise in futility to estimate how extensive the practice of manumission, in which slaves were finally rescued from bondage.

Since the fish market was largely confined to the harbor locale, I was compelled to gloss over the industry, failing to pinpoint the methods for preserving fish and, indeed, the very functioning of the fisheries themselves, whose wont, beyond such typical fishes as tuna, pilchard, red snapper, sea-bass, mackerel, flatfish and swordfish, was to bring to market periodically still other denizens of the deep.

I slighted too such matters as oxen and horses as draft animals, albeit in general, the former drew the plow and the latter the wheeled vehicle, the wheels for the great part being spoked and the chariot itself made of bronze; the scope of cosmetics, jewelry and furniture making; the state of the arts and crafts—not excluding building, sculpture, murals, vase painting, literature and music; waterworks and the primitivity as to "piping"; disposal of garbage and other waste products, undertaken without tapping the available water supply (whose diminution often the bane of cities). Like the Romans, these townspeople seemed to have a preferment for "trenches" in lieu of "open dumping." This meant—except for slum parts of town—they could minimize the health hazard and malodor problems.

To be true, the sewage challenge seemed more astringent overall for Carthage than Rome since the latter was blessed with proximity to that substantial river the Tiber together with its tributary streams. The Romans early had learned how to turn the marshy grounds between the hills of their city into an effective sewage system. This, no doubt, was capped by the Roman endeavor to convert one of the river's tributaries into a canalized underground about three hundred years ago. This sewer, named Cloaca Maxima, became Rome's greatest. Devoid of such a topographical prize, Carthage had to make other arrangements.

I also skirted methods of entertainment for the masses in general and social life among the upper classes in particular; the degree of use of table and kitchen utensils and pottery in the home; the nature of the oligarchic order to rule over Carthage; the precise techniques for measuring time and the calendar year and the prevailing weather patterns; the humdrum side of life, where in this city-state daily living was pretty much a grueling struggle for existence; the virtual absence of sports, beyond arena antics by "gladiators" 28 (and save for an incidence among sons of the elite, related to their training as military officers in the state) owing to the rigidity of climate; and status of architects, administrators, shopkeepers, craftsmen, educators, scholars, priests, engineers, navigators, sailors, commanders and mercenaries.

With respect to mode of dress I had little to say, other than to stress togas and gowns of cloth and similarly fashioned turbans, preponderantly white for the men, set in Tyrian shades for the women, and designed to accommodate a mild climate. In appearance the women were mainly divergent from the men in the use of cosmetics and coiffure.

Lastly, I was afforded but scant opportunity to conjecture how widespread were such societal practices as divination, incantation and necromancy and those of occultism and demonolgy. My untutored guess would be that they were an integral part of the going religion.

I was soon to discover I had made an almost fatal mistake. Crossing town, harbor-bound—an effort predeterminedly-arranged, since it was mandatory I embark that same night—I encountered midway across *Cartagena Square* one of those disingenuous patrols. In the twinkling of an eye I reversed my course, with a dozen Carthaginians or so in hot pursuit!

I adopted what might be dubbed "the pocket method of evasion" this time. I entered a public edifice, as if it were a sort of sanctuary, then speedily withdrew from a side entrance. Once the pack had gotten safely ensconced inside the structure, I sprinted back across *Cartagena Square* and, finally made it to safety.

But, ironically, even though running the course withershins had outmaneuvered that particular posse, suspicions were almost at once aroused over my sudden presence on the *other* side of the square. Intertwined with further patrol performance, I soon had another sprint engagement to meet! By this time I was thoroughly soaked from perspiration, all the way from my ill-fitting turban right on down to my Carthaginian cache-sexe garment. But how could one outsmart the dilemma raised by sudation in this sort of climate?

In due course the artery I had selected led to a rather sizable open area. I quickly concluded from the unmistakable effluvium that this was the section of town to accommodate the municipal stables. And certainly the mammoth structures soon to come into view seemed like nothing less than the Augean Stables!

While there were very few horses in evidence, in addition to some cattle I spotted three or four elephants attacking with their trunks piles of forage. Stable hands were also walking other elephants, in what presumably was the daily constitutional. The stables themselves were rock structures with many apertures spaced at intervals all the way up to the eaves, doubtless to discharge the need for ventillation. As a furtherence of the precaution the manure mounds did not adjoin the stables. Also proximate to the stables were a series of open sheds containing bails of hay stacked high. The entire compound was placed at the central part of the great square, its periphery being marked by a timbered fence.

Largely due to the fact the installations were guarded—very likely they were under the jurisdiction of the Carthaginian cavalry— I adhered to the prudent course of skirting the area. Any interest in scaling the fence was quite dampened, anyway, since I had noticed its timbers seemed to be scorpion-infested! Although this entailed an unwanted detour, I soon had resumed my course on a direct line for the harbors.

More and more patrols seemed, at an alarming rate, to be in the offing! I simply had to conduct my itinerary with more caution than heretofore. With one matter I could be thoroughly pleased: the fact

I only had to contend with foot patrols—so many Carthaginian horse having been committed to the Spanish campaign.

At one point I was compelled to take refuge in some sort of Canaanite shrine, and I fell to wondering about my Carthaginian friends, especially in light of their more cryptic practices. As to the edifice itself, it appeared to vouchsafe the usual architectural marriage between Greek and Phoenician. Complete with dome and buttresses, the inner chapel was the standout section. Tinted in gold and silver—it permitted a rather truncated picture content to blossom forth belatedly most gloriously. Before the main altar was a lecythus. Putatively, this held the ashes of Dido—rather than some romantic oils or perfumes. It was in chambers on either side of the altar that the non-eucharistical rites were performed. Inasmuch as this city-state was allegedly founded by a woman, I was minded to check a mite further as to just how the ladies fared in this very bastion of yesteryear.

The status of women, while far from apotheosis, seemed remarkably high, if I circumvent concubinage and the oldest profession itself. For the typical married woman the role was ambiguous. She was strictly monogamous and subject to sundry taboos anent behavior in public. Otherwise, virtually as privileged as her husband—only was she debased by the fertility rites. Concubinage was institutional—(sparked by a struggle for existence arduous, to say it mildly) the trading of loss of status for the easy life. As for the "harem" that was the sport of a few "nabobs" alone. Eastern customs seemed to have been diluted by the symbiosis of Carthaginian mercantilism. Then, again, it was possible numerous oriental practices were not transplanted by the original settlers of Carthage due to the lore that Queen Dido herself was at hand to supervise the embarkation. Such a matriarchic tradition could but enunciate a bettering of the condition of women in general.

To the exoteric it shortly became manifest that, barring specified quarters in town that catered to lower class men who could not afford concubines, the demure conduct of Punic women for routine living was radically at variance with that adhered to throughout the occult religious practices at the shrines of Baalim. Inasmuch as the fertility cults of the orgiastic type reached back into Phoenician history, it was not unbefitting to witness being practiced by the citizenry an import version of the veneration. Nor the fact that at times of fertility rites the modest, unassuming, scrupulously-clad appearance of the women miraculously changed. And the accouterment became not loss of chastity or infidelity but sanctitude and consecration! Babylonian-style, the virgin let her hair down and the housewife did her thing.

I bethought myself these fertility rites had something going for them at that . . . one could almost have wished to miss an appointment with an outgoing bark . . . especially one questing after sulphitic experience. Such the lure of a night of promiscuity, of utter uninhibited lasciviousness; the disrobing in those temples, the intermingling of the sexes and the acts performed—all to honor a goddess! Even though explicit enough—what I witnessed in just one shrine alone I would not tempt ennui by ampliating further with details as to the sex activity consummated under the idolatry, since that would be tantamount to asking Melkarth, the god of fire, what he thought of the Syracusan tyrant Gelon!

H·B·SARGENT

Chapter IX

Yet speaking of Syracuse (for so long ruled by the tyrant Hiero II through fealty), there seemed evidence things were taking a turn for the better between that city-state and Carthage. This, no doubt, reflected the onrushing Roman insurgency, which *nolens volens* must have been causing their misnamed "Sicilian allies" considerable perturbation. With Rome and Syracuse locked in together on a long—hardly friendly—border in Sicily (after the Syracusans had come to terms with the Roman horde in the First *Punic War*), surely Carthage had a golden opportunity to woo Syracuse away from her tatterdemalion alliance with Rome?

In Carthaginian experience one thing stood pellucid enough. Syracusan ethos was clearly to be master of all Sicily. Any foreign encroachment there was regarded as a threat to her survival; the beautiful island was, in sooth, her front and back yards, or so this would seem the line of reasoning she was wont to adopt.

Thus, in the present scheme of things, Carthage—out of Sicily altogether—had become Syracuse's *natural* ally. Not Rome—now posing a challenge to Syracuse's very existence. By coalescing against Rome, therefore, these two internecine rivals could in one fell swoop compose their differences and with dedication try to contain the Roman expansion—doing so with or without the cooperation of the unreliable Uticans.

The coast being clear at last, it behooved me to press on. Leaving the shrine, I was heartened to note that it was already fairly late in the day. Before long the gathering shadows would loom up as an indispensable asset. I yet had one major hurdle to surmount; I had to get through the city gates! Guided more by a sense of approximate direction than any special attention to specific streets, I shortly traversed from an inconsequential side street into an inordinately curving narrow throughway. This I presupposed, for its arcane aura of significance, to be an artery to link up with the open area by the main gates, at the very least an avenue that would expedite my arrival at the time-imbued Great Plaza and, thence, immediate egression from this celebrated bastion of North Africa.

My musings regarding best ways and means for leaving town turned out presumptious in the extreme. At one point, in fact, yielding to a near-fatalistic rationale, I wondered whether I were not actually caught up in a labyrinth.

With a jolt to hot-galvanize my innards—I stumbled front-a-front upon an ornery-appearing patrol headed precisely my way! The commander seemed a man of no mean rank—perhaps even that of a centurion—inasmuch as he displayed more insignia than I had heretofore detected on the raiment of any officer. Almost instantly, as a sort of insinuendo to his militiamen, he drew his sword, which he had in a sheath corded around his toga, and—to the cadence of Punic ejaculation which eluded me—commenced to move the bronze weapon about not so much menacingly as ritualistically. Instinctively, I deduced this the procedure to be adhered to—according to the manual—when an officer was about to make an arrest. As by a process of osmosis, his followers raised forth their javelins—this latter deed interacting a much more threatening mood.

Beneath my breath—I seemed somehow to whisper "Come, good Sirs, what will all these Boeotian ballistics profit you?" But just then I had no inclination to elevate my voice or transcribe the words into Phoenician!

With gawky leg movement—I was about face in a jiffy—and out of sight, thanks to the pronounced crookedness of the street. A nearby pattern of sound, something not unlike a ricochet of myriad echos, told me that the kinematics of pursuit had replaced the mere rituals of making an arrest.

54

I thrust myself into the first side street to come along; and, as it bechanced, there soon stood on the right a wooden gate ajar, impressive for its contour and carvings and set in a high-walled fence.

Almost convulsively I darted through the gate. But to my unalleviated horror I discovered it was a barracks! The guard at the gate shouted for me to halt. I turned around only to find it too late to retrace my steps. The warning had alerted other guards by the gate, who were armed with javelins.

I dashed for the nearest barracks, one of several such buildings lined up end to end and in rows. My vision took in the presence of a complement of other structures in the spacious area—most probably functioning as commissary, refectory, arsenal and so on. Even as I gained the building entrance I could see the whole place was coming alive!

The barracks was a simplex wooden structure with a row of cots shrouded in sheepskin and cattle hide extending from either side and separated by a central aisle. As a dormitory its decor easily matched its fragrance—far from sweetness and light or fresh perfume! Luckily, it being daytime, the building was unoccupied. Sprinting in at one end I tore through the structure, with several javelin-wielding guards on my trail. Summarily leaving that barracks I entered a second one—only this time I grabbed beds apace, thrusting them into the aisle as I went. I soon gathered from the Punic outpourings that this expedient was making matters much more tedious for my pursuers. My further consolation was that only the soldiers guarding the compound were armed, with most of the garrison on duty elsewhere, anyway.

The tactic—in any event—permitted me to gain on my foes. On the assumption they would pursue me into the third barracks—I abruptly sprinted around the second barracks and re-entered it. I soon became an unkown pursuer of my pursuers! Catching up with the last of them I slammed two Carthaginians together and at once became the possessor of a gleaming bronze javelin. This I straightaway used as a club on a pair of heads that betrayed a trifle too much curiosity about who composed the rearguard.

The soldiers kept exclaiming something that sounded like "Go-wah-wee!" Thus, to assist them in the assumption I was one of the boys, I tried out my Phoenician accent: "Go-wah-wee, Go-wah-wee!'' We proceeded in this manner to the last barracks, with me bringing up the rear.

It was here that I had to bid my friends adieu. At an earlier point, a glance had apprised me that the building at the further end of each row of barracks was quite near the tall wooden fence. This made it automatically my target in the circumstances. As the militia rushed into the last barracks, I tossed away my javelin and shinnied up the structure. Once obtaining the roof, I sprinted along the top of the structure, with the soldiery going pell-mell beneath me. Shortly reaching the end of the building, I leapt onto the fence and was safely out of sight even before a single arrow could be fired. So ended my brief career as a Carthaginian soldier!

The game plan now was to effect progress toward the downtown area and avoid retracing my steps—which might take me all the way back to the Sanhedrin itself, for all that I could be certain of.

At this point, perspiring like a gentle spring rain and panting like the foregathering of storms about to let go, I streaked up the comparatively straight side street, which I had regained a little ways from the barracks, dodging pedestrians as I went, leaving them uniformly transfixed, staring after me in disbelief!

I soon became cognizant that the roadway was grounded on an acclivity and that I was ascending a secondary hill, one of Carthage's several topped by big Byrsa.

Convinced I had shaken all pursuers, for the nonce at least, I reduced my frenetic pace in order to catch my breath and simmer down. Moreover, in spite of the hill, the direction seemed toward the harbor. Refreshed by the period of relaxation, I began musing over the dilemma of this great city. Clearly now, it was endangered by Rome. But cardinal to the success of whatever counter-measures Carthage adopted, was unity on the home front. And disunity revolving around two great factions was the order of the day. One was the Barcine party, to which Hannibal (and his late father Hamilcar Barca, its founder) belonged. The opposing party was headed by the very wealthy Hanno and associates. While the former was known for military talent and patriotism, the followers of Hanno were more numerous and had access to more money. They also had been accused of corruption and exacting excessive tribute from the provinces.

To compose differences almost irreconcilable was, thus, the real crisis facing this town. Only with harmony at home could she hope successfully to woo Syracuse and eventually activate a joint hegemony between them in the Western Mediterranean. Such a ploy might also permit Carthage to match off Syracuse and Rome in a geopolitical sort of way. But just the feat of overturning the unrelenting ambitions of the Romans would prescribe that these two towns must finally master the discipline of co-existence, which their Greek and Phoenician antecedents had failed to do. But in addition to a cohesive Sicilian policy, it was incumbent upon Carthage to address herself to the Spanish campaign. At this juncture, her most pressing requirement—far from divisiveness over it—was, paramountly, at the veritable level of the Sanhedrists to back Hannibal to the hilt!

In the course of my town meanderings, I had happened upon a small plaza with as its centerpiece an imposing statue. Offhand, the figure seemed the similacrum of the eponymous ancestor of the Canaanites, the spiritual progenitor of the Phoenicians. Apocryphal though it was, legend had it there once also reposed in this very plaza a statue of Aeneas, no matter he had left Carthage to marry his Lavinia; but the high priests had ordered it destroyed following the loss of Punic Sicily to Rome.

Somehow, the episode struck me as a portent.

My movements had been impeded not merely by the need for caution. Progress was hampered by city commotion itself, especially in the downtown section. Whether this was owing to Baalat or the state of war was not clear.

In any case, much commotion there was. Far from being merely an aspect of a thriving commercial environment, say at the late day rush hour, it was marked by much hubbub and tumult, on the streets and throughout the thoroughfares—racing chairoteers (whom one had to dodge for dear life!), horsemen, crowds of noisy pedestrians, bedlam at every turn.

Frantic fair Carthage—preserver of the great traditions of commerce and colonization, following in the footsteps of Phoenician and Minoan, and, of course, the Greeks. Surely she deserved better than Rome was one day to mete out . . .

In the morning I had been able to see how much grandeur and artistry had gone into this walled town. A great system of ramparts combined with the pattern of hills to give Carthage, to all seeming, an impregnable defense, her sole vulnerability, perhaps, on the harbor side.

On a rise in the northwestern part of town, situated not far from the seat of government itself, was a well-spaced cluster of fine villas, which housed many of the great families of the city. Circumjacent the homes of the elite was a stunning ambiance of fruit tree orchards, shrubs and flowers, arranged pleasingly-terraced and with overall landscaping. Generally the more indigent members of the community resided down by the commercial centers—which, reaching down to the main gates, fanned out in juxtaposition with warrens, where dwelled the most lowly of the populace, along the periphery of the harbor.

From the hilltops one realized a fine view of not alone peninsula and bay, but of many of the most salient temples and municipal buildings. One could also descry the section of town whence obtained the function of *bread and circus shows*. 29 There was prominent an impressive structure, that would be an open amphitheatre, and nearby a coliseum-like edifice. The harbor was literally a forest of masts and a great lattice-work of oars—pinnace and bark, galley and fishing boat; some sailless, others rigged for one or two sails; some resting at anchor, others moored along the wharves; still others gliding to and fro in the great entryway—entering or leaving the port.

It must be kept in mind the city of Carthage, inclusive of extramural suburbs, was situated on a large peninsula, whose cynosure happened to be Byrsa hill, on which the original citadel reposed. 30 The settlement in effect was based on a natural bastion between the Lake of Tunis to the south and the marshy plain of Utica to the north.

The peninsula itself was attached to the mainland by means of an isthmus at the mouth of the Catadas river into which the Lake of Tunis debouched.

Due to a possible quirk of nature the topography of the harbor (actually, there were two, linked by a canal: one military, the other commercial) spelled its location some three-fifths of a mile south of Byrsa. The harbors hinged the great peninsula to its three mile link with the mainland, the final part of which was a narrow tongue of land. Along the south side of the isthmus stretched a spacious compound of dockyards. Here was quartered the maritime pulse of the city-empire. Here the mighty war-galleys, including trireme and even quinquereme, which for so long a time had left Carthage mistress of the Western Mediterranean, and the merchant fleet that had brought her into touch with all parts of the known world, were built and outfitted.

Even though the hill was a mere one hundred and ninety-five feet above the sea its panoramic view was supernal in the extreme. With mountains, amaranthine at the horizon to the northwest, two great promontories from which the peninsula seemed equidistant formed the flanks of the Gulf of Tunis they sought to enclose. Then beyond the vistaing of city sites whether public edifice, statue or outer wall or harbors sporting great quays for unloading freight, an artificial lagoon and jetties, there quickly evidenced were the slopes and plains, featuring fields of barley and corn, interspersed with vineyards and patches of cactus, and further off the serenely un-dulating plains reaching westward even unto Tunis.

Abutting on a section of the quayside were sheds or lodges. These quartered the galley slaves when off duty. Unlike the mer-cantile market place, which was situated inside the city wall, the slave market was contiguous to the harbor, probably since it pre-dominantly related to manning the galleys. With respect to matters funebrial, Carthage was not conspicuously unlike her sister cities of the classical age—albeit the final canons of each community were according as its religious persuasion. While the practice of cremation was becoming more prevalent, due to (Sicilian) Greek influence, she had her necropolis and lesser burial grounds (even near the temple of Eshmun on the plateau of Byrsa, just like the huge cisterns to the east, was manifested a complex of Punic Tombs of state officials).

As elsewhere—given the times—the extent of community in-volvement depended on rank of the deceased. While steeped in pagan rites, a similar public participation applied to the institution of matrimony. The religion of this Phoenician people was polythe-istic, supporting a pantheon of deities. Thus, there were other, less prominent, gods to assuage: Astarte and Adonis and household deities comparable to the Roman *lares* and *penates*, and very likely some other *"genii* and *di"* ascribed by many to Aeneas, since allegedly it was he who brought Trojan idols to both Carthage and Latium. There further seemed extant the practice of attending the sacred fire at shrine altars. This consecration, conducted under the auspices of Melkarth, was performed by virgins, comparable to the Roman vestals.

Chapter X

At length I emerged into an exquisitely-laid out square, whose most arresting attributes were an imposing shrine and a handsome serpentine stone wall on the farther side, demarcating fine clusters of cypress and balsam fir: a strange beautiful park right before me!

A fastidiously-wrought bronze gate, which was ajar, I immediately could see was the orifice into these stately stands of trees, in conjunction with a chariot and horse-beaten path that wound through them.

To the vexation of the gatekeeper, sitting idly on a fine-hewn bench beneath a sloping overhang, whose expression until then had been one of sheer vacuity, I betook myself into the arboretum and strode up the roadway. Gradually enhancing my pace, as I ascended the sloping terrain, I soon beheld what amounted to a veritable condominium of stately villas!

Vaguely the thought crossed my mind that if nothing else the homes of the elite might function as a buffer between me and my tormentors. However, glancing back but moments before the gateway fell from view, I at once descried the presence of a patrol in the plaza, ostensibly interrogating the gate keeper.

Almost in the role of desperado setting his face against the real possibility of capture; and as one not *thoroughly* prepared to come to grips with the methodology of Punic torture . . . I sped up that sloping hill as if my very life depended upon it!

But after a few moments—in a flash an unpresaged thought crossed my mind. The estates of the merchant princes were *out of bounds,* both to the military and police, leave quite be the citizenry at large. I was grateful for the intermezzo this would afford me, as by now I was laboring under disabilities and almost *desperately* needed time in which to cool off.

With a sigh of relief I reverted to a walk. Mopping my brow and assaying to regain my aplomb, I began to thank my lucky stars for the presence of this haven. I still remained on my guard, however. Scanning the road ahead as a precautionary effort at one point, I detected a twain of chariots heading down from the villas. Answering to the dictates of discretion, I sequestered myself within the inner recesses of a sturdy grove of cypresses. Soon thereafter, without further ado the charioteers passed me by.

The various arborial groves shortly came to a halt alongside a vortex of surprisingly verdurous lawns—flanked on the opposite side by flourishing orchards. The lawns distended variously to well-groomed terraces of the score or more villas that were in the area.

On one of the lawns a lively crowd of teen-age boys, appareled in the usual toga, turban and sandals (for their superior quality a dead giveaway they were children of the nobility) was assiduously engaged in a physical sport. This I finally deduced was called "All-Apple" or "Catch the Apple." At first glance one might almost have assumed it a strange admixture of tilting at the ring, pushball and hop skip and jump . . . all rolled into one!

Earlier in the day I had gleaned some fragmentary information on the matter from some Punic script.

It seemed the group of players were obliged to divide up evenly into two teams; these duly assumed their positions on opposite sides of the field. Prior to that two urns had been set at the foot of each of two apple trees. Into these receptacles were carefully counted an identical number of apples, but always leaving room for more. This prerogative was usually discharged by correctly assigned custodians, generally adults designated as "tribunes of the game," since they automatically served as "referees," as well. These dedicated gentry together with a modicum of male members of the families involved along with a few patrician guests comprised the body of spectator attendance.

But the game "Catch the Apple" itself could hold little significance were it not for the provision for "the throwing apples," a
fairly indispensable commodity for a contest immersed in the toss-
ing of fruit! And, of course, sports activity in Africa (exclusively
a privilege of the elite) was traditionally confined to the early morning or late afternoon, and only sparingly indulged in during the
summer.

Working with one of "the throwing apples" the game would thus
begin—following an esoteric procedure for selecting the team to
have the first throw. In the instance of the game being played just
then, I could not decipher how they resolved the opening move
problem, since I arrived too late on the scene. A further game
requirement mandated all "apple throwers" to meet a minimum
height—any throw not to exceed the length of a topgallant mast of
a two-sailed bark then six apples were forfeit to the opponent.

In any case, once the game got under way the rules decreed that
whenever a team player failed to catch an apple, the forfeiture was
one apple to the adversary. When time ran out, either due to the
encroachments of the mid-day hour or the intercession of darkness
itself, the apples in each urn were assiduously counted by the
referees, and the side with the most apples carried the day. The
final instruction of the game applied at this point and it was the
most fanciful of them all!

The prize for the winning team—always formally pronounced by
a prefect—was the much-coveted honor to wreak, at appointed
place and hour, some mild sadistic punishment upon the losers,
such as their having to run the gantlet *au naturelle* while their
conquerors zestfully snapped cypress boughs and the like across
their backs and hindquarters—or, congenerically, crawl through an
avenue of their opponents' legs, receiving a like attention. The
victors could virtually name their pleasure. In the event of an un-
pardonable "sudden death"—the unlikely circumstance where a
team could not meet a forfeit—the prize was greatened threefold.
Similarly, the dictates of the game entitled each team captain, in
the interest of improving individual performance, to employ
unspecified forms of discipline on behalf of its most flagrant "apple
droppers."

With the *stakes* so high, it ineluctably became a game played "for keeps," and it was not difficult to account for the sparsity of nonplussed glances thrown my way as I strode by. Looking over the field, I could only think—at that moment in time I needed exercise of this toilsomeness like a hole in the head. But for sheer sameness what a tedious sport it appeared to be, how they were able to endure its gruelling monotony I could not fathom!

Watching the game a bit, I was struck by the curious requirement that each toss of the apple must be preceded by a hop and a skip. "The jump"—if it existed at all—was interchangeable with "the throw."

At one point the apple soared in my direction. Despite the fact two players were zeroing in on it—inexplicably something goaded me on to foolhardy act, being aware, I supposed, that I could pick the apple off over their heads, if minded to do so. Executing the wild scheme with an alacrity that surprised me, I instantly snatched the apple out from over them, performed a hop and a skip (I trusted graceful feats). Then, with all my might I let that red ball of fruit fly. (Upon the feel of it, in retrospect, it seemed a kind of cross between a McIntosh and a Grain Smith.)

Probably by far the highest throw of the afternoon, it proved too much for the bemused opponents. Some luckless performer got a hand on it but could not hold onto it. My "gambol," nonetheless, paid off.

To my astonishment, both teams set up a spontaneous shout to a man, the while waving their arms, clapping their hands, jumping up and down. The éclat of the field spread its contagion to the spectators, who almost at once climbed to their feet in a standing ovation!

By way of acknowledging the compliment I waved my arms in the manner of magistrate or consul after having completed the investiture of high office. This evoked a further spate of laudation. At least I had made a few friends while in town! I remained very jealous of the vital necessity to preserve my aloofness, however.

Continuing on my way, I fell to pondering the recent happenings. While the hiatus was reinvigorating for more reasons than one, I could not shake some nagging doubts about getting out of this abode of the elite in such a way as to be properly redirected toward the harbor, enabling me, at the last, to reach my destination, the red-sailed bark, in good season.

I just had to hope that fate was not playing fast and loose with my aims. There was so much of an unspeakable nature to evitate that I could not even pretend to maintain an organized hegira. Rather, I was more to be likened to a tiny bark being buffeted about in a great Mediterranean tempest. But hope springs eternal; so I rationalized, with as much firmness as my flagging spirits might summon, that what I was to lose on the roundabouts I would make up on the swings.

I soon drew near some of the fabulous villas of the great families of Carthage; children and parents were lolling about in the orchards and gardens, as if there more to survey the impending sunset than anything botanic.

Almost like an odorless fragrance they could but effuse an almost palpable disinterest to befit members of the uppermost social stratum. Certainly, in the *arrondissements* of the aristocracy, conspicuous leisure had long hence been established as the norm.

The view, truly magnificent at any hour of the day, was for me now to serve a more practical purpose. The contour of the harbor and the whereabouts of the main city gates, which I also managed to discern, ameliorated my sorely pressed understanding of directions.

I also was able to identify an open area alongside a portion of the massive city walls. This would be the Great Plaza situated opposite the main gates.

It was often called the palladium of Carthage, for once upon a time there allegedly was placed there a statue of the goddess Pallas Athena. This Aeneas had brought with him from Troy. Unluckily for Carthage even as the fabled voyager was bidding Dido a tender farewell, the palladium, now become the guardian of the city, was at his instructions being hoist aboard one of the departing barks. 31

Still and all, a view so gorgeous entertained distractions enough. Almost at once I caught a clear portrait of the far-famed Temple of Eshmun: a handsome, indeed awesome, edifice! 32

Constructed in the tradition of the Phoenicians of metal, stone and timber, it limned a striking silhouette against the sky. Most insistently prominent was the great entryway leading to courts that majestic colonades enclosed.

The columns also divided, in magnificent settings, the naos into side aisles and nave. From portico to roof top a spellbinding creation! With reluctance I snapped to. I must not let things of great beauty detain me. I had some important business to complete. I resumed my circuitous journey.

This, inevitably, did not deprive me from espying other Carthaginian landmarks. For instance, I was favored with a much more consequential view of the old citadel. A rather amorphic and forbidding structure, overall, its turrets were hardly distinguishable from the very walls and balustrades. It must have antedated the outer ramparts of the city herself literally by centuries. But even though antiquated and for the great part in desuetude (inclusive of a spacious stable area used only when the city was besieged by foe)—save for water and food storage and dungeons that were euphemistically termed "pacifying chambers"—it yet stood out as that penultimate court of last resort should enemy ever breach the outer defense system.

Its innermost campanile, which might only be ascended by a ladder chain, thrust itself skyward, beauteous, unbowed—a mystical beckoner to good Samaritan, from genesis to armageddon, who might not wish upon this town a far happier fate than she was one day to suffer—grandiose in its stark way as it towered over the old fortress, commanded a view of the entire harbor side of town and much of the city herself.

Chapter XI

This structure, I learned to my edification, also housed the main water reserve of Carthage—the grand reservoir, as it were, which the city had constructed with great diligence, since its peculiar significance lay not in normal daily use of water. Urns and cisterns disseminated about town fulfilled those requirements. The reservoir, in effect, for dimensions so exceedingly large, a subterranean lake, was chiefly intended to be at the ready in the event the city must withstand a prolonged siege, the kind of crisis sometimes to convulse, without warning, the great city-states of the age.

With rain a somewhat limited commodity in North Africa, it was an imperative not alone to use water sparingly but to fetch it from all manner of tower and dwelling top when it did favor the city. Periodically, a portion of the captured water was toted in small urns into the citadel and poured into the reservoir. At such times, to sustain daily use, supplementary supplies had to be transported from the Atlas mountains. However, excepting periods of extreme drought, water was quite freely allotted for the state gardens and use by the elite in general.

The well-nigh reverential attitude toward water was reflected even to the elaborate plans for the construction of the reservoir when it was built some two to three centuries ago. Carved out of the sheer rock of Byrsa, with provision for symmetrically-spaced pillars to secure the rock ceiling and with air pockets to avert water staleness—a great storing place was in due course achieved, one which the city had had to depend upon on more than one occasion.

Although my interest in this overriding structure was scarcely atypical, I trusted that it did not approach anything like morbid curiosity. For I could not efface the unfettered fact that if anything went wrong with my doch-an-dorrach it might serve as my unpleasant home for a little . . . At length, due to the peripatetic pattern of my gyrations, I found myself striding up a path, flanked by well-tailored beds of flowers and leading to a most symmetrical dwelling. A one level complement of rooms and halls (the "high-rise" concept, embracing more than one floor, practically was ruled out—since it would have to be contingent upon the availability of the so-called inside staircase, and that structural innovation had not come to Carthage) the domicile seemed to be fashioned around a great atrium, with entryways abutting upon it front and rear and with a harmonious layout of side rooms on either flank, delineating the character of wings. To anchor the building, there were flanking pillars at each "doorless" entrance. The notion front and rear entrances had no application at all.

A bevy of handsome—and most alluringly-perfumed—young women, wafting large kaleidoscopic-colored fans, stepped by, staring at me—I might add—with unvarnished amazement! As if to quadrate with their dark boreal beauty, the group were flawlessly-attired in headdress and toga, done in gorgeous shades of purple, blue and crimson, and dainty sandals. Carthaginian women at the upper-echelons of the social order received perforce—I was to discover early in the day—all the exaltation of social acceptance. Indeed, even beyond this, there seemed prevalent an almost inexorable air of deference. Very likely this was in part the outcome of the fact so many of them were so remarkably easy on the eyes!

It might even beg the question, at that, if I professed unduly that my irreconcilable dilemma was that I was simply too excessively large to be courting these petite dolls of antiquity: the plain facts were that I had an excuse or two that were not so transparent.

While regarding myself as visiting mariner merely passing through town, it was plain that I was already being targeted as a fugitive at large by the city authorities! Add to this the language barrier (although "love" is pretty much as universal as music) and the pressing need to quit town that very evening or face the gravest consequences—there was no chance to socialize with these fair damsels of the Mediterranean world.

Still and all, whither bound were they at this hour of the day? Did they peradventure have a date with Goddess Baalat in the shrine by the gate leading to the estates of the elite? Were they then embarked on keeping a sanctimonious appointment, one wherein with sublimity and extreme unction they would systematically disrobe and with ecstatic abandon submit themselves to the fertility rites?

A flirtatious thought crossed my mind. What a disarming group they would make in the *altogether* and what occult secrets of rapture might be exposed—whether projected as they were or as devout maidens of the faith prostrating themselves before Baalat at the most passionate levels of surrender . . .

With an alluring smile I nodded quite pronouncedly to them, but to small avail. Their response, but an extension of the stare, in short order became the catalyst, for as by pre-arranged signal they all burst into titters.

Smiling approvingly, this prompted me to quote Byron back to them in Greek—selecting the words "thou who hast the fatal gift of beauty." On the strength of this they regained their composure momentarily, then went off into the giggles again, only to wind up in hysterics! In this latter state they were truly a disarming group of young women.

Conjuring up the most aristocratic *tournure* I could muster I shortly entered the domicile by way of the portico. This introduced me to an outer hall that duly opened into what had the smack of being a magnificent atrium. To my pleasant surprise, I thus far had not stumbled upon so much as a living soul. Actually, I must take exception to these words. For no sooner had I entered than I was confronted by a pair of Barbary apes. These shy creatures, which I had noticed a few times about town, were apparently popular as pets in Carthage. Not really apes at all but macaques or, if you wish, short-tailed monkeys, this pair soon betook itself to a more secure hiding place.

The atrium proved to be a fine arcaded and becolumned hall; the rectangular section interior to the columns featured open sky and, for its centrosphere, a circular pool of water, seemingly alive with little turtles. Olive trees and ferns embellished the corners of the grandiose room and upon the walls of the arcade were rather striking murals whose significance in my haste I could not even dare to guess. Instead of leaving the building by the anteroom to the rear—due to the fact the mansion seemed to be deserted, owing to the hour of day—curiosity nudged me into surveyance, a brief probe of the annex to the left.

I soon had my doubts as to the wisdom of such a detour. Crossing a hall area I ingressed into a spacious muraled room. To my no inconsiderable discomfiture, it was occupied! Reclining on semi-circular horse-hide couches were some half-dozen of the more vintaged members and guests of the great family. With almost inordinate solicitude servants situated close by wafted palm tree leaves over these lofty personages, no doubt to make the trials of heat and humidity a trifle more bearable. Meanwhile, upon my entry, from the far corner of the room a gray parrot, undulating upon its perch, delivered a harsh tirade over my unannounced presence.

Electric signals, somehow going wanton, at once apprised me my unceremonious intrusion was not a matter to be completely overlooked from the standpoint of the illustrious household. A telescoped course in ultra-self-discipline, and there would very likely not be the remotest chance of a repeat. Really all so elementary! I did not opt to debate the point.

Nonetheless, I was determined to adhere to a facade that might delay any sounding of the alarm or that sort of crass "reprisal." Pretending that I had so rudely entered the room for the sole purpose of paying my respects to these noble dignitaries, I waxed my most august; thence bowing with that stiffness to dissemble deference ne plus ultra I recited two or three Greek proverbs.

Banking on this as a useful fabian performance, after the proper civilities of withdrawal, I was out of that room in pudding time and into a spacious outer chamber at the rear of the mansion. Strangely, the calm of the place to the contrary, through a sort of ectoplasm of doubt, I had the feeling the whole nidification was coming alive!

Vacating the premises via a side exit, I stepped out onto a fine grass terrace that eventually adjoined an elaborate floral garden, then headed for the protection of trees, my immediate avenue of escape. I had more important things to do than inspect flowers and rare plants. Passing another sumptuous villa, I shortly advanced to the end of the complement of stately structures and was back among cedar and cypress stands, with the demarcating fence line of the property in view.

As previously noted, I had been somewhat puzzled as to why the outer periphery and especially interior itself of this loosely drawn inner city of Carthaginian nobility was so ill-guarded. Yet I had only to hearken back to my matinee activities along lingual lines to educe the probable reasons for it.

There prevailed about town a sort of unwritten understanding that the confines of the great families of Carthage were out of bounds to plebeian, to be trod upon at his own peril. In an age when the uppermost stratum of society would brook no trespassing by commoner, punishment for matters of this ilk to captured culprit was ministered by example wherein specific consequences were de rigueur.

Thus, in imposing savageries upon victims of one stripe or another the patricians, unwilling to countenance any personal affront by the plebs since so jealously they guarded their pre-eminency, were not above resorting to harsh retaliatory measures. On such a stage, where the prerogatives of the elite were concerned, no counterpoise of liberalist rationale could be presumed even to exist, leave quite alone carry influence.

With this climate the status quo, the incontrovertible rules of the nobility asseverated that any interloper caught on (or off) the premises must suffer, if a Carthaginian commoner, thirty lashes by goodly corded whip, or if captive or slave, forty lashes and at least three brands about the body, said punishment to be meted out in a public square. As for an intruder who chanced to be a spy—well, I would rather omit the exegesis to apply there.

Paradoxically, I could not altogether fault Carthage for this. In an age of rampant slavery and fairly rigid stratification of the social order it was a sine qua non that in order to perpetuate an assertorial role in society Draconian rules for the commoner must be devised; and these pertained especially to the areas of personal safety and protection of private property. For their force in deterrence they were eminently pragmatic, thus preserving the privileges of the elite.

Moreover, since the days of Alcibiades, the Athenian expedition to Syracuse and the Peloponnesian War, with the attendant nebulosity as to personal loyalties—even the function and character of espionage and scouting had become more precisely defined. By the time of the see-sawing Punic-Romano struggle that commenced forty-six years ago, eximious arrangements had greatly narrowed the possibility of survival once a spy was caught. I was not so besotted as to be unaware that "tender mercies"—classical age style—would exert themselves with a "pre-examination," not unlike the incipient treatment often reserved for a heretic in the Middle Ages, with sole intent to loosen his tongue, deterging him—as it were—of all useful intelligence (in my particular circumstance this would have proved a trifle *complex* due to language barriers!) to be followed, once the "patient" was expendable by a *coup de grâce* thoughtfully arranged in a spirit of "punishment to fit the crime." And the mutilated remains would not be so much as graced by a catafalque.

But with regard to the treatment of plebeian, as indeed of enemies of state, it was not a question of removal of inequities in societal affairs. They were a fact of life. Rather it was entirely a matter of whether they were so prohibitively unjust as to be counter-productive. In Carthage, at least, they were more in equipoise with a remarkably sibylline concern for public welfare—a precursor of *social conscience* itself.

A civilian order had vaulted to power and the merchant princes, like the patricians of Rome, once were lowly. Thus, while the patricians and plebs embodied a degree of ambivalence, and in extenso resultant fluidity, for both cities, Rome was to cast hers to the wind with the advent of the empire, and Carthage was to see hers evaporate even as she was effaced. This was an affirmation that in more than one way Carthage, like the indigenous civilization to have spawned her, was ahead of her times. If she had only been

72

able to scare up a hermeneutic scholar or two to address themselves to the gravity of Roman expansion!

Because of the emergence of class-structured society to accompany the growth of city-states, to round out the supplanting of absolute monarchy, autocracy or even theocracy, extenuating circumstances undoubtedly attenuated Carthage's—by later standards—seeming lack of humanity. Although there were materialist influences also, which worked both ways, it was even by the crass standards of the ages immediately to follow no charitable era. Yet Carthage, due to the genius of Tyre and Sidon, was as liberal and humane as Rome at her best. The commerce of the Phoenicians had alleviated theocratic influences. The high priests of Carthage played a lesser role than those of most Semitic nations. Again, mercantilism had helped to evolve a pioneering dualism that asserted a wholesome *disestablishmentarianism*—popularly understood as the doctrine of separation of church and state.

While the Punic priestcraft continued to be influential, real power was vested in an elite class who ruled by proxy. Carthage contoured as much a plutocracy as an oligarchy. Here Rome and Carthage were in similitude.

As the Roman senate with the passage of time came to control the consuls completely, it itself became dominated by plutocrats. Even though in fact Carthaginian government was endowed with both a great council and popular assembly, they had virtually no decision-making role. Actual power lodged itself in the hands of the judges and the chief magistrates, functioning on behalf of the great families of the state.

But this was the opposite route to some other forms of government of the earlier contemporary or later periods. In Egypt, for instance, there had prevailed for so long that rubric—high priest, king priest and god incarnate. Rome under the emperors was to attempt caesaropapism (the temporal ruler usurping church functions) and later the Eastern Roman emperors were almost to perfect it. Contrastively, the Pharaohs of ancient Egypt were *in esse* high priests who had commandeered sovereign power. And Syracuse had her benighted spells under the Gorgon's head of the tyrant, remindful of the ordeals of ancient Athens.

In spite of my unabating anxieties due to my predicament, I could still register a degree of tolerancy toward Carthaginian cruelty, which after all was hardly incommensurate with the age. Moreover, even the exigent manner in which the aristocracy imposed its rule made considerable sense given the times. For Carthage was still as proximate to an "open society" as any since the Greek experiment, a brief interlude or two in Syracuse following banishment of tyrants and a faltering effort in Rome during the halcyon days of the republic.

Chapter XII

Small wonder, there was a complete absence of that serene sense of *sine ictu*—no scuffles with guards or the police, no mad chase or derring-do—which seemed from my angle of view almost a run of the mine activity in Carthaginian streets since the Roman bombshell was promulgated in the council hall. Unmistakably, in spite of the presence of a powerful faction in town that perforce would prefer to sheathe the sword, the fact must remain Carthage was in a state of war.

On the other hand, there was ominousness enough in the reading of this immediate quiescency, allowing for the rules of the game (which were somewhat more taxing than those governing "Catch the Apple"). Unwittingly, I had sullied a well-near sacrosanct encyclical of proper behavior while in Carthage. This was what in all my innocence I had violated; and, like the law of the Medes and Persians, it could not be redressed, short of "doing penance" Carthaginian-style. To say *no thank you*—in the face of such an abhorrent verdict—might almost incubate a tonality of the academic; a man bound and gagged hardly had many options open to him.

Frankly, I was skeptical that many transgressors of these princely realms were *ever* caught alive. After all, what would be left of them to be bound to a stake for a cat-o-nine-tails flogging or, if need be, branding—after mounted horsemen had let go their arrows in search of them or a beastly pack of attack dogs had polished off its long-overdue dinner?

As a sort of prescience that this elitist abode was soon to turn out to be a hostile milieu for me—I had just beheld the specter of what appeared to be well-armed guards advancing in the direction of the paddocks and kennels.

My high tea with fond friends was over!

Almost methodically, I quickened my pace. I was determined without further ado to quit this side of town, whose insidiousness seemed but a codicil of ultimate entrapment—and once more head downtown in the direction of the main city gates.

The way matters turned out, this was to prove a timely dedication. In the twinkling of an eye I was at full stride—for luckily I had glimpsed what was coming—if what I was hearing should have proved inadequate! Such a cacophony of howls I never had heard before. A final, no holds barred hundred yards dash brought me abreast of the serpentine fence, and *truly* I hurtled it almost as a pole vaulter! I must thank the thin line handicap (a *headstart*) in my favor for making it at all: no sooner had I cleared the aristocratic park than the hirdum-dirdum really reached its apex. The ugly pack drew alongside the masonry and let go with toothsome howls of frustration. My thanks went out to that lovely, lovely fence . . .

With the equestrian detail at a good distance still, a rash thought crossed my mind. On the instigation of it, I seized from near-hand palm trees a few leaves which due to the season and weather patterns were easily relinquished. Then, drawing out matches, I lit up. First one, then another and another, until I had a fistful of fiery boughs. These I graciously wafted across the fangs and hides of my intemperate pursuers. Fire, like money, even in ancient times had a way of talking—even though for the canine community the word should be "barking." In brief time the entire pack seemed to have gotten the message . . . and, as one dog, they stampeded out of there, probably in the direction of the approaching detail of mounted guards! I did not tarry further to see just what sort of confrontation might ensue.

Still and all, belatedly I was persuaded to reproach myself, for I should have understood why the great families could justify their independent system of law and order, rendering their inimitable bastions of the home off limits even to patrol or policeman. They were well-endowed with a protective system of their own.

Continuing my peregrinations . . . instinctively I felt my momentary *piece de resistance* was to covet an out-of-the-way street or two, keeping fairly before me the precise location of the main gates and the artery leading to the harbor which I had just confirmed. Of course, a cautionary approach was chiefly propped by the thought that those equestrianized guards of the estates might elect to scale the walls and pursue the search into the city proper. Hopefully, the yapping, snapping responses of the "attack dogs" would relieve them of any ideas along these lines. But I was not going to bank on it one way or the other! Indeed, my anxiety hardly abated at all. I entered a darkling little street, fully recognizant that, while now I might be exposing myself to hazards of a totally different character, for the nature of my exodus from the great estates I had most probably launched an alarum of such dimension as not to be quelled simply at those serpentine borders.

Such misdoubts should have been cause enough for trepidation. Perennially, a pedestrian, like a foot soldier before cavalry, was a helpless entity when faced by mounted police—without even speculating about dogs. Yes—the dogs! Delving one step further, there was always present that background condition that had sustained itself through so much history. Whenever a commoner offended a nobleman—more often than not he had to ultimately run for his life. Propelled by this sobering, I hoped not, premonition, I decided the principles of the question called for action rather than quodlibets. I vowed at the very least to arm myself somehow and straightaway! . . . selecting a weapon if possible that would prove extremely wieldy, whether for brandishing or smiting. Casting about uncertainly, I soon drew abreast the facade of what purported to be a cabaret.

In the course of the day, I had become cognizant that when soldiery patronized such places for hard cider or sundry wines, the regulations enjoined them to honor an orderly process of depositing *all* weapons at the entrance. These would remain safe under appropriate surveillance until retrieved. This practice turned out for me the answer to a prayer—even to the point of selecting a weapon I could handle with ease in almost any emergency.

When the guard's attention was drawn away to a vociferous

interchange over some picayune concern, I saw fit to take fullest advantage of the diversion by expropriating a weapon idoneus to my immediate needs.

So while not even *extra muros* I had acquired a bronze, implacably-curved and most sturdy scimitar-like weapon—which, should worse come to worst, could with equal effect be used as a lightweight club. Unbeknownst to me at that moment it was to become for quite a while my fast friend . . .

Moving at a steady pace—oddly *en rapport* with my rate of perspiration—I meandered along the jejune street. Abruptly it came home to me the sheer quiescence of the artery was untoward for that hour of the day. Had the city folks hereabouts taken shelter . . . on the assumption some ominous visitation was in the offing?

Then I heard them . . . voices out of hell . . . the baying hounds rounding the corner into the street . . . three ferocious-looking critters coming my way lickety-brindle. Instinctively, my innards went down that deadly hill toward bottomless gulf. I felt the muscles in my hand tighten over the scimitar handle . . . and almost instantaneously I was atop a parapet alongside a footpath, with clear intent to advantage my position to the utmost, given the extremity.

Scimitar at the ready—those few seconds seemed an eternity. With a final bound the attack dogs came alongside the wall . . . a chaotic commingling of yapping, snarling, leaping and baring of fangs ensued. One of the beasts managed to get too close, and I felt a searing pain in my right calf. While giving vent to a degree of "bloodletting," luckily no muscle tissue was jeopardized.

Perhaps on the strength of this initial setback—with all my might I laid about me—raining down razor-knife edged blows upon those demoniacal heads and unhandsome hides. Hideous Cerberus of Carthage, would that I assuaged the score once and for all!

Although a far cry from the splendid triumph of a laboring Hercules, I was almost desperately determined that those three well-fanged mouths would not seriously impair my scheduled departure from town. This was the *hour of cause*—canine threats or no!

After a few moments, one of the hounds, bleeding from a number of gashes, veered off, and with a final display of puissance I sent the other two packing—their howls and snarls now having simmered down to whimperings and every expressed indicaiton they were anxious to be gone.

To be certain, it was really only a Mexican standoff—and nary a minute too soon! Virtually at once the distinct rhythmic hoofbeat of a cantering horse caught my ear. As it grew more audible I became convinced that other horsemen followed, along with more dogs..!

Immediately I crouched low on the parapet, scimitar firmly held—awaiting the arrival of the lead horse. The rider promptly turned into the street, automatically reducing his pace.

This was my cue; with a great leap I was on the road, grappling with the rider's spear and politely pummeling him the while with my trusty scimitar. The horse, bridling and skittish, finally reared, and the stunned rider toppled back over its haunches and onto the roadway.

Perhaps I was only succumbing to the gossamer of the environment—but I had become aware that my marked disparity from having become so involved in violent acts, on the laser beam of my desperation, I had quite managed to obliviate. I hoped not a brainwashing shortcut to brutality but a temporary outcome of adversity.

The cacophonic refrain of the contingent of galloping horse and dog now about to turn the corner was my penultimate goad to alacrity!

Grasping the reins of the affrighted steed, I stepped into the stirrup and mounted the beast. Then, shamefacedly plying its flanks with the heels of my shoes, down that street we went apace into the more commercial depths of Carthage. Once or twice my stampeding horse brushed shoulders with pedestrians too slow to catapult themselves out of our way, reminding me of some of my own contretemps of the day. It was at least a bouquet of relief in one sense to be off one's legs for a while . . . and yet, with deference to my having been faced with a crisis as strenuous as "my kingdom for a horse," I could not be entirely persuaded the unpredictable tergiversations of fortune would be altogether fulfilled in my favor aboard that galloping horse.

Shifting into another avenue before long—in order to throw my immitigable pursuers off the track—we soon emerged into what had the earmarks of a bustling produce marketplace.

Inasmuch as this Carthaginian landmark (legend had it that Queen Dido herself once dubbed it "the Fruits of Aeneas"—which may have intended an ironic connotation) led obliquely into the Great Plaza, in combine with the fact I was quite desperately trying to enter that last place before exit from town as unobtrusively as possible, I decided this would be the consummate spot to tether my horse; it would—possibly significantly—serve to confuse my adversaries when they arrived there. If I entertained any weighty insights as to the behavioral activity of noblemen, once rancour had been aroused, inevitably they would put in an appearance in this produce market before long. Like the elephant of Africa, a box on the ear was an effrontery they would never forgive.

Tying the horse to a post, with dear scimitar well-concealed under my very damp toga, I nonchalantly feigned a passing interest in Carthaginian fruits and vegetables.

With no more than a glance or two it became abundantly plain that the townspeople, as an outcome of agricultural skills, were efficacious in the matter of preservation of fruits by drying—notably, Muscat raisins, plums and apricots. While the array of fruits on display was broad, including apples, pomegranates, pears, peaches and grapes—and I did not miss the hefty bins piled high with sundry types of almonds, walnuts and pistachios—even the vegetable department had no apologies to make. On view was a variety of legumes, featuring beans, greens and gourds; also, spinach, asparagus, beets, wild carrots, carob and onions; with nearby a plentiful supply of herbs, spices and honeyed sweetmeats.

The market seemed governed along mercantile lines rather than free enterprise. However, the produce folk worked their food stands with nimbleness, helped by the use of measuring equipment, such as scales. They also demonstrated an admirable prowess in the area of dissuading light-fingered customer, for apparently as often as necessary they would, with merest wrist motion, bring down on exposed knuckles the full weight of pointedly-serrated rod.

Picking my way through the shrill crowd, I unobtrusively strolled out of the market place and into an avenue that would betake me ultimately to the city gates.

In concurrence, as an added insurance or rather as a further precaution, in line with my persuasion to keep my itinerary as circuitous as possible, I had decided not to remain in any single artery too long. All, I supposed, on the assumption my elitist pursuers might yet be *seriously* on my trail.

With this strategy in mind I left the avenue—but not a few paces from it, I was at once accosted by an ornery group of swarthy scoundrels who gave utterance in some sort of "pig" Punic. I got the message, especially the dagger their leader was holding very flirtatiously in my direction—or in more anatomical accents—at the *throat*.

With a quick pace backwards . . . in one fell swoop I had my scimitar out there from hiding . . . doing its thing! With fierce unabating gusto I slashed about me, and in almost no time the cutthroat gang was gone.

Returning to the corner of the main avenue, I paused briefly to cool off. I was rapidly losing my appetite for out-of-the-way arteries—but still had to contend with them as almost equally unpleasant alternative to circumventing challengers that with almost deliberate regularity I would come face to face with on main city streets.

Chapter XIII

Two cats rushed in front of me (startling me somewhat, more than likely a by-product of my most recent nerve-racking activities). Never had I beheld so many of the furry bewhiskered creatures. In this seaport grimalkins were highly prized, doubtless due to Egyptian influence on Phoenicia—a popularity scarcely diminished for the unmistakable presence of rodent and insect.

While cats seemed to have the run of the place, their canine cousins were much restricted—my particular brushes with them to the contrary. Often they had assigned duties to perform—especially in the suburbs, which I had visited in the forenoon. Diurnal tasks, such as safeguarding flocks of sheep and goats; nocturnal chores, such as protecting the farm herds and draft oxen from marauding packs of wild dogs or prowling big cats—rendering such services not rarely even to the inhabitants themselves.

I had made a brief sortie by chariot into the country, with East Numidia as the caudex. Even though ipso facto an aborted jaunt—it was an unforgettable experience! The city of Carthage was civilization itself compared to the proemial conditions that assumed command once one strayed beyond her confines. But this was only true to form, since it was the age of enclave.

In the natural course of things—to the extent I personally encountered them—Libyan provincials were relatively more predictable than their tempestuous confreres of Numidia. This was perhaps in part due to some salient cultural anomalies between the two Hamitic peoples.

While the Libyans were exposed some to the burgeoning sophistication of Alexandria, the Numidian people were hardly more than at a tribal stage of advance. Yet, with allowance for this primitivity, they were unquestionably an agile and assiduous people, evincing marked virtuosity of horsemanship and, for the manner in which they parted with arrows in battle, an equal expertise in mercurial dispatch. In spite of the xenophobia many Numidians were quick to reveal, and the nucleation of outlaw bands among them, it was the environment to be encountered beyond the reaches of imperial Carthage in lieu of the inhabitants that was the overriding, if not forbidding, entity. 33

Once beyond the farm belt, which coveted the Mediterranean shore, an insistent change in the ambiance could not be disregarded; the aridness of much of the countryside, the bush lands above all rain-shy even in the cooler months and baked so piteously by the sun during the long hot summer days; the never-minishing swarm of insects around the water holes—mosquitoes, gnats and flies; the all-but camouflaged presence of lethal ant hills and hornets nests; the ever-vigilant lammergeiers, falcons and vultures. Perhaps even more mete were the daytime hazards posed by the unwelcome incursions of fauna. How things stood in the country neighborhood at night could but be a topic of sheerest conjecture!

Even by day, occasional dogpack hit dimensions to exceed one's wildest fancy. In this back country, facing dunes and desert to the south and grassland, branched shrub and cactus to the west, they roamed not in packs but armies once the heat of the sun was gone. As for the game animals of the habitat, such as leucoryx, mohr and other antelope, they were conspicuous by their absence, no doubt due to the plethora of carnivore in the area at that time of year. Thus, they too seemed propelled to the hinterlands along with the Atlas bear and the wart hog.

In marked contrast, there also lurked about in the bushveld tarantula, scorpion and the deadly garter snake—the very last a far cry from those New World harmless fellows, since these ringed creatures were truly venomous.

In the morning, in a barter that relieved me of some valuables I had on my person, I had negotiated successfully with a chariot and harness tradesman for the rental of a chariot complete with two spanking spry horses. One horse was a bayard, the other a piebald. The first demonstrated an example of a strong admixture, the other an ancestral type—I adduced—of the later Arabian breed. And how effortlessly they made my chariot go! Their smoothness, effusing superb timing and great strength, was ticketed as an in-dispensable commodity the way events were to unfold.

Thus, no matter how peripatetically inclined I may have felt, my meanderings were foreshortened by unheralded facts of the envi-ronment. There was, for one thing, not remotely adequate time to seriously penetrate East Numidia, even though my curiosity had been aroused over Cirta its capital, where the satrap Messinissa held court. Yet even if I had been able to reach my destination what hospitality would have been in store for me?

For another, it was judicious (if not mandatory) I bypass Tunis, which bestrode the main route to Cirta, inasmuch as it was reputed to be a hotbed of piracy. But my efforts to circumvent the town proved near-disaster itself! I was brought up short by the veritable obstacle race I dipped into or, rather, immersed myself in—once off the beaten path, a genuine jungle of roving bands of pirates, stray packs of wild dogs and sundry other predators (which even though nocturnal creatures per se seemed to be active by day). In fact, I was flabbergasted by the size of the dogpack that at one point tried to close in on us. There were also surreptitiously about big cat and roving hyena. Lastly, as though in a role to orchestrate all the hazards, there was the immitigable heat.

My preparations for the little sally now complete, I left Carthage via the main gates. These augustly set in the gargantuan walls of the town were fashioned of bronze and emblazoned deeply-en-graved panels, celebrating Carthaginian glories of a bygone day.

Following along on the chief artery, I soon passed the lowly squatters' community festering there just beyond the city wall and shortly penetrated the great farm belt.

At once there was evidenced a very considerable agricultural development, embracing the artificial watering of arable soil, but seasonally reinforced by the rainy season which had ended in the early spring: tracts of land confined to wheat, barley and grain, others to fruits, vegetables and vineyards (with unmistakable proof Carthage had not neglected date-palm cultivation nor that of the fig and cherry tree), still others functioning as enclosed pastures for flocks, cattle, oxen and horses.

The cottages were well-groomed, seemingly sturdily built, and situated amid orderly stands of cypress, savin and Atlas cedar, with contiguous gardens playing their role, appearing to me—in passing—to feature such flowers as jonquil, lotus, grass-of-Parnassus and a species of narcissus, haphazardly interspersed with such shrubs as heath, tamarist and desert fern. Finally, the ubiquitous opium poppy made its presence felt.

There were people about and those near the roadway almost unalterably stared in our direction. I just had a hunch they were not looking at my steeds! Farmers actively tilling the soil with oxen and plow or working in the farmhouse yard, which seemed to pulsate with goats, swine and fowl; women—not a few of whom were breastfeeding infants—attending to barnyard chores; children, at play or flitting about, and occasional roadside vendor.

In contrast to many of the inner city structures, which were composed of stone, the suburban buildings were mainly mud brick. Once beyond this area evidence of civilization became more sparse. This was a matter to apply even though the highway was sufficiently traveled by day to negate potential threats by marauding animal or human.

The farm belt sector of the community was measurably more stable than either the unspeakably impoverished warrens immediately outside the walls of Carthage or the outermost reaches of the city, which were contiguous with the provinces, where there was little more than a semblance of law and order. Not alone were the farm lands properly linked up by a meaningful system of roads and communication, but there was a constant protective enterprise by the constabulary. In marked contrast, at a certain point beyond the city pale such hardy inhabitants to survive were almost incessantly plagued by pirate or predator—challenges that could only be interdicted by the military, when not otherwise engaged. This was the prevailing syndrome for the Carthaginian empire and elsewhere.

Nevertheless, the special treatment of the farmers reflected merely common sense. Were they not, after all, the providers of much of the food supply? It must also be borne in mind Carthage had gained a relatively sophisticated state in the science of agriculture. Whether the matter pertained to the raising of cattle or horses, the laying out of groves of fig, date or olive trees, the planting of wheat and cotton, the developing of some of the greater vineyards of the Mediterranean world or the engineering of a vast irrigation system in a relatively dry section of Africa—the Carthaginians were unquestionably past masters. Add to all this her elephantine fisheries and breath-taking botanical gardens (which included many fruit trees) and Carthage easily became the foremost food Mecca of the ancient world.

I had held to the chief roadway linking Carthage with Tunis. My stratagem was to accomplish a U-turn around the town once I approached her suburbs. So far on the comparatively stable main artery matters had been quite uneventful. A presumed normal flow of chariots and a far from spectacular presence of pedestrians, orderly but usually armed, percolating from one habitation to another along the periphery of the highway.

I soon adopted what seemed a useful way to divest these folks of their mistrust. Inasmuch as to a man they were wont to stare at us in astonishment, I would acknowledge it by raising my arm and gesticulating amicably in their direction. Almost invariably they replied in kind.

My chargers were serene and cooperative, with commendable patience ignoring the constant buzzing of large flies, and I was beginning to enjoy not just the novelty of my experience but the outing itself. Even though in a chariot one was obliged to stand, I ere long found myself in a whimsical way wondering if I might not be getting some good training as a potential sulky driver!

Notwithstanding, it was still pretty steamy stuff—guiding this twain of horses out there in all that heat. Before the morning was done it would become a nexus in my thinking. Oh, for a cold shower once back in town! Out of the question—no such facilities. How about a lukewarm tub, then—there must be some soap around? Surely some of this must have threaded its way into Africa after being first processed in southern Gaul over three hundred years ago?

With aim to probe further the rationale of Carthaginian destiny, I waxed cognizant regarding some odd coincidences—some yet to eventuate—that had caught my fancy. The actions of Magistrate Hanno were one. This was probably the most powerful leader of the conservative land-owning party. Indeed, it had been only a matter of his control over the purse strings, culminating in his refusal to pay the mercenaries (even though their levy was in arrears) that provoked their revolt, pursuant to the earlier Italian War. This even had Carthage endangered for a time, until Hamilcar Barca —at the defile of the axe— suppressed the insurrection. Yet, assuredly, if the deliberations of the Sanhedrists, of whom he was one, were any criterion, Hanno was once anew assuming obstructionist role?

Perhaps not the least ironical of eventualities was the fact that the namesake great grandson of Marcus Porcius Cato, a stoic philosopher in his own right, was of all people to do of all things in of all places—commit suicide in Utica! Peradventure, this violent act of self-immolation was symbolic of what Horace was to have in mind when he sang the words:

> O mighty Carthage, lifted higher for
> the shameful downfall of Italy!

Since time redressed the balance (after all, did not mighty Rome herself cave?) this might sound like a nugget of comparative anthropology. More than likely Horace was bemoaning the loss of the Roman Republic, while perhaps subconsciously owning to just a wee pang of conscience for the dastardly deed Rome was to commit.

All of which reverted me to the elder Cato, that man who hated men alike things, especially when cheerful. Even though putatively a good soldier in his earlier days, he had only rancour for Scipio Major . . . just as he was prolongedly antipathetic to Hellenic culture. Our misanthropic senator was plumb chauvinistic in his grim and grueling way. Certainly his entire political career, manifesting a warped patriotism, stressed the fanfaronade of Rome at the expense of all neighboring peoples.

Plutarch, when he entered the canvas at a later date, would doubtless accord with this. But so much trembled in the balance!

Ultimately, though, it was not the mouthings of a perverse propagandist that counted, but the fortunes of war itself. These determined the attitude of allies and the provinces, even of dormant foes.

Quite a spell before the war just launched was to terminate Masinissa of East Numidia would lead a defection to Rome of certain of the Carthaginian provinces. As for Utica under *the tall one* she would not so much as deign even to consider a league with Carthage. For her inchoate hostility she made a mockery out of any pretenses of cordiality toward her neighboring sister state.

Nonetheless, Carthage and Utica still had in common congenital Phoenician ties. Such as a tongue virtually interchangeable (even though the twain were scarcely on speaking terms), a collocation of social and pragmatic customs almost identical and a profuse Tyrian talent for commerce, navigation, engineering, architecture, boat building and seagoing culture par excellence. They also clung to pronounced similarities of spiritual practice, and their order of guardians was identical. The citizens of each city worshipped gods of Baal, along with the lesser deities, where the pattern for both communities was deemed to be indistinguishable.

As for background, this presupposed for the deities of ancient Semitic peoples, notably Syria and Palestine, a Canaanite source and, belike laterally, one for the Phoenicians themselves, who subsumed the Carthaginians and Uticans through colonization.

In extenso, there obtained an authorship of fertility of the soil and enhancing of the flocks, whose worship were agricultural festivals, the rites of oblation, animal sacrifice and, finally, human offerings.

At some point where husbandry and grain fertility became inseparable from people fertility, human sacrifice seemed to have been introduced in this religion of the son of Ham. The primogenous practice—namely, the sacrifice of first born children to the god of fire—dates way back in Tyrian experience. 34

What were primordially mainly agricultural and husbandry rites seemed across the centuries to have broadened themselves into degrading cults of human fertility and sacrifice—whose rituals were conducted at the high places of metamorphosed gods of fire and war. Variously, both Carthage and Utica indulged these practices,

even though on the orgiastic side more tailored than the ongoings
of typical Roman holiday, even prior to her imperial heyday.

Chapter XIV

Abruptly, I detected a squadron of horsemen out in the bush to the left trotting along briskly and pointed toward Tunis. My mild curiosity was engaged. Who were they? I could verify they were neither army nor police cavalry. Why did they eschew the main artery this way—opting for being far from the madding crowd?

I should have imputed more significance to the incident, but I was engrossed with other matters. Anyway, they soon dropped out of sight.

In due course the circumambiency of the main artery began to change. It became clear my chariot was approaching the outskirts of Tunis. Evidence to support this lodged in greatened activity beyond the immediate flanks of the road itself. I espied occasional abandoned shack smack in the bush, then the presence of well-protected homestead. At a far remove to the right, I spotted another equestrian band, at that particular moment.

Shortly after, a flock of demoiselles flew directly over us. This bird, the Numidian crane, was fairly small in size. Perhaps their abrupt presence in the sky signified something—an augury of trouble ahead, maybe? More cottages (which for their painstaking similitude were cruder even than those of Carthage-oriented farmers, ranchers and vendors) revealed themselves by the roadside. The time was thus ripe for my detour. Vaguely I cast about for a halfway-acceptable tangent to remove me from the highway.

My ploy was to take an informal road to the left, which proved to be no more than an enfeebled country lane. My chariot, following the game-plan, commenced the long U-turn. This—I subsequently realized—was at the very least an ill-starred endeavor! Of course, at the outset it was all insular and serene enough—save for that hot sun, which already had begun to interject itself as something of an infernal nuisance, especially since it generated considerable thirst. But, notwithstanding it was practically verboten to take one's chances with Punic water, throughout the day I did manage to mitigate dehydration by sipping wine occasionally.

My mind continued to wander as I bethought myself about things Carthage and of that city-state's world. There was always the danger of exercising the apocryphal, whose verisimilitude could but be grounded on possibilities innate in the passage of time. Yet with even this admission allowed, logic seemed only to point up the likelihood of inexorable change.

The circumstance of an asherah being invariably placed next the altar in a Canaanitish high place, suggesting an even earlier tree worship, and the common denominator of the massebah in Semitic experience, attested to this. Pellucidly enough, there was implicit in such subject matter multiple politico-religious influences, a complex ethnology, inclusive of extensive patterns of cultural admixing—all transpiring over a protracted period of time in Asia Minor alone, without delving into the *cradle of nations* itself.

Simulacra between the two city-states of North Africa aside—as for what really ruled in the living Carthage, to say nothing of competing Utica as well, it must not be oblivionized that all chroniclers of the period and the centuries directly to ensue were either Roman or Greek. After that all records were muffled by the mystery of time.

While scholarship of the period must needs admit to bias, especially that of the Romans (although opportunistic Greek historians openly pandered to Rome), the irrepressible fact of the matter remained: Utica herself left no cultural body of memorabilia; perhaps this could have been accounted for by the Arabian sacking of the town around 700 A.D.

At the risk of treating of the unfathomable, one might conclude Carthage too was not seriously engaged in literary art. While this

92

would appear the case for Utica, it was belied for her sister city-state since it was a known fact her great library was leveled when Carthage fell in 146 B.C. and the manuscripts of her archives preponderantly destroyed or, as some scholars maintain, thrown to the irresponsible, but then liberated, African colonials.

It was rather a dearth in the plastic arts that seemed to be common to both towns. This stood out in bold relief from the multinominal features of religious practice both communities experienced, not just via the graven images of Baal-Ammon or Moloch and Eshmun, but from the worship of the ancient Canaanite goddess Asherah to the cult for Astarte, a Semitic goddess of fertility, beauty and love and the most important of the Phoenicians.

Moving at a fast trot, everything seemed placid enough, with no more ado near at hand than locusts flitting about and occasional red lizard slithering from view. But tranquillity could hardly be the rule in such an environment. Indeed, we had been off the main road a scant ten minutes when to my mortification I discovered a mounted band of pirates on my trail! Shades of that first group I had so nonchalantly ignored. In that agonizing moment my fervent wish became the return to the main artery, and thence back to town. This way of journeying to East Numidia was a foolhardy circumbendibus! Strictly for the birds.

Only minutes before I had detected a flock of vultures eating carrion, and there seemed to be striped hyenas about. Although they were at a distance, they impressed one as roving about in packs, probably *ex cautela* a safeguard against wild dog. Aware that this species has been mistakenly deemed a scavenger, even though actually a hunter, I did not attach much significance to their presence since they rarely attacked human beings and preferred antelope and the zebra to the horse. However, it should have been my cue.

What led up to the eventuality of a rotting carcass? What was the fundamental milieu to prevail here? Just what sort of jungle was this, encompassing both man and beast?

I could tell my tormentors were not of the military—not just the missing insignia but the style of weaponry they deployed. Moreover, the military did not go gallivanting around the countryside, particularly with so many Punic horse in Spain.

With no choice in the matter I worked the whip and we rose to a gallop, and it was a bumpy session we were in for on this oxen lane! My pursuers were still almost three hundred yards back, but my realest anxiety was over the fact we were sheering further and further off from the highway. I had somehow to contrive to run the course withershins.

Suddenly, the horses began to bridle and snort—even to whinny—raising their goodly maned necks upon high and shaking their heads worriedly, as if to register disapproval of my driving. Such commotion rent the chariot, already careening crazily, with heavy vibrations.

The explanation for their agitation was not long in being discovered. Scarcely more than an eighth of a mile away a pack of wild dogs loomed up coming our way with unambiguous celerity!

While they were—not unhappily—a piece of real estate away from the chariot, they looked quite like the wild dogs of the south, which roamed in packs over the savannas of Bechuanaland and the Transvaal. I could be almost certain they were not ridgebacks of the far south, as their backs carried no discernable pattern or trace. But, no doubt, the most appalling thing about them was their sheer numbers! They seemed to demonstrate the coalescence of a number of packs, which they were apparently wont to do when the occasion warranted—perhaps there had been a drought driving their regular prey to the hinterlands.

What had been butterflies in my middle turned into a gnawing ache; and a buzzing sensation sifted through my head, as though to apprise me of this moment of truth.

The winding road held to a pattern of skirting thicket, but was occasionally ravined. We had entered such an area where we were obliged to go around a substantial concentration of growth, which tapered off into a rather uncluttered ravine. Firstly, the dogpack was removed from sight, then moments later the pirate band itself disappeared. Both groups were yet a goodly span away, but the gap was narrowing apace.

This was our golden chance—perhaps our very last! Reacting almost compulsively—I reined in the horses, then veered chariot into the shrub-strewn glen—with intent to effectuate, under cover of the surrounding thicket, an about-face and a return to the central artery. The terrain, almost instanter, became an added hindrance. Yet we had to knife through the busy section to protect our concealment.

Accordingly, we held to a fast trot; and even at this modest pace the chariot hardly played on velvet! My strategy was to time the U-turn so as to evade both pirate and dog. Our sweep had to be at once recondite and broad; and it was almost too broad, as my chargers were quick to adumbrate. To my further discomfiture, without forewarning I shortly beheld in the very next meadow not one but a whole pride of lions lolling in the grasses and eyeing us with great intensity!

The bayard, especially, seemed in an affrighted mood, reflecting unmistakable panic—meanwhile, the piebald whinnied and half-reared.

At all costs it was necessary to prevent an uncontrollable stampede. Tightening the reins and with organized use of the whip I stepped us up to a canter. Another anxiety soon to register on me was the capacity of the harness to withstand so protracted a strain. In order to insure my equilibrium in a chariot, now so tumultuous with a pace so onrushing, I had wound the reins tightly around me. This adjustment eased into equipoise the compulsion to catapult me out the rear of the chariot with the forward thrust movement of the stampeding chargers.

But my realest concern, with each passing step, remained not how fared the horses but the rig. Would the harness hold? What if either the yoke or traces snapped—or, better still, if the belly bands broke—what then? Two madly dashing horses would go galloping off—leaving little me and chariot to the tender mercy of lion or dog pack.

After a time of almost undiluted agony we scaled a moderate rise, where the bush thinned out. I calculated the pirate band would in due time be more removed from the highway than we, though we could not prognosticate that it was also to serve as a buffer between us and the dogpack. The elevated locale placed at our disposal a fair view of the whole area, and this confirmed our expectations.

The pirates were approaching the bend in the lane where we had turned off. I saw something else too and all but gasped!

The dogpack the while had been zeroing in from almost the opposite side; ostensibly the timing was such that neither band had spotted the other. Collision course seemed only inevitable!

Directly I witnessed an unimaginable scene. Something to be an episode of prehistoric days. At once the horses of the pirates commenced to rear and scream. Then the dogs appeared—snarling, lunging, nipping; and the weirdest melee conceivable ensued!

The pirates struggled to fire their arrows—but the effectiveness was interdicted by the crazed horses, one of which stumbling was summarily gainsaid the right to rise. At least two riders were thrown, instantly to serve as fodder for the dogpack. The remainder of the squadron in a great panic stampeded out of the ravine, heading wildly into the bush with half the pack snapping at their heels!

H·B·SARGENT

Chapter XV

We had passed the crest of the rise but were in time to witness yet *another* spectacle. As it chanced, the direction of the horses brought both horse and dog into fairly close proximity with the family of lions. At that point a rump band of the dogs left off the chase and surrounded the pride. Some bushes momentarily shut off my view. When I next got in a glance a titanic struggle seemed under way. The big cats, however, soon made the bold venture counter-productive. Bunched protectively at bay, they roared defiance, the while fitfully lunging and smiting at the sleek elusive dogs. Perhaps as many as four or five of the pack came a cropper, receiving the full force of a lion's paw across their epidermis. Sporting backs half raw, they staggered off, to all intents and purposes *hors de combat*.

After that the dogs waxed canny and kept their distance, almost as if to admit the prey were too formidable for them. From our fading grandstand position, the skirmish appeared transformed into a mere probing operation. Possibly, in a weird sort of way, it was all but a diversion to enable the panting overheated dogs to simmer down.

We at length gained the secondary road. This placed us merely a trifle over an eighth of a mile from the highway. But only a fool would have exercised the luxury of breathing a sigh of relief. In that country above all! A dose of skepticism from my angle remained unabated. What new danger lurked there in this Godforsaken demesne of the overwrought wayfarer? The strange confrontations had ministered to us the chance to buy vital time. Nothing more. Indeed, at that exact moment a pack of some thirty to forty dogs, having picked up our scent, was closing in on us at the dead run!

With not a moment to lose (the dogpack was less than three hundred yards away) I worked the whip with almost reckless fervor. And my sturdy but frantic steeds, snorting and bridling to beat the band, went up to a gallop. I was grateful for the ameliorated terrain. The chariot was no longer bumping about, just oscillating hazardously. Still and all, we had a piece to go, and with that inexorable pack on our tail this was no picnic. In due course we drew near the main road. Just at about that time, almost by design, the dogpack slowed its pace and shunted off the country lane. Some bushes momentarily intervened; when I next surveyed the locale the dogs had betaken themselves elsewhere.

Nevertheless, I could not soon forget those lusty fellows: agile, spry—the embodiment of primeval savagery; hot red tongues hanging like tiny drawbridges from panting pulsating throats; beady alert eyes to stand the pack in good stead; strong trim bodies, ever equal to the toils of pursuit. A race of hardy creatures that would sooner devour than wean even a Romulus and Remus.

A moment or two thereafter we swept onto the highway, my still affrighted horses rearing convulsively and emitting astonishing amounts of perspiration and froth. I felt a badly needed respite was due—the moment I became convinced our antagonists were in absentia.

In line with this I reduced the gait to an easy trot. Notwithstanding we once more traversed an established, well-maintained highway, whose flanks were spangled with hamlet, habitation and outpost, more trouble was in store for us before we returned to Carthage.

We had been back on the main track for half an hour or so when an untoward incident arose. It was perhaps owing to our radically foreshortened pace, to give my steeds some crucially needed recuperation. Whatever instigated it, it was another almost frightening recrudescence of danger.

Even granting I had outmaneuvered the pirates and the dog-pack—with panegyrics to unadulterated good fortune, my worthy horses and very likely the lions—how beneficial would all this have been if I were but to wind up with a dagger in my heart?

We had progressed a few miles along the highway when I discerned dead ahead, and closing in on us faster than I could have wished, one of those potentially scary mob situations. Ostensively, to the uninitiated there were pitfalls even on this indispensable artery.

The glaring question gripped at my throat: how to penetrate a rabble of this character—a boozed-up band of Numidian rowdies . . . if not a road maintenance gang acting out of true? Having had enough of "off-beat trails," I was rapidly becoming disenchanted with "on-beat paths!"

Even without their palpable aura of ugliness—communicating with these earthy folks was next to impossible. They seemed to give utterance in a species of pig Punic, interspersing the business with a rather gutteral African dialect. It was a mélange totally beyond my phonetic position.

I nerved myself. Come hell or high water—through the intervening mob it had to be—although, just privately, I was starting to wonder whether I might not make it back to town at all.

Almost instantly moving my faithful chargers up to a canter, and grasping the whip at the ready, we met the mob foursquare.

With a cacophony of menacing shouts they tried to bring the chariot to a halt then and there. While one swarthy fellow seized a bridle, three more leapt aboard.

With a smacking thrust of the elbow I sent one sprawling to the ground. Taking hold of the other two, I cracked their heads together, and they plumb withered away. One crack of the whip promptly loosened the hand on the bridle. Meanwhile, two more hooligans assayed to attack me from behind: a well-placed kick silenced one and a sharp jab with the butt end of the whip to the neck finished the other.

Then, shifting the sting of my swirling rope to my two trusties, the chariot literally hurtled forward and surged through the crowd, scattering it helter-skelter. And away we went to Carthage town!

On second thought, it was not all that romantic. There was little time for sanguineness given the pattern of kaleidoscopic misadventure. To say nothing of wear and tear on horse and me.

Having disposed of the unruly Numidians, I reduced the pace once more—largely out of empathy for my overburdened and most heroic friends. Again, we assumed an easy gait, which we held for quite a while. This vouchsafed us both, after such arduous enterprise, a measure of much needed relaxation. I was dripping perspiration and for the moment at least quite exhausted—my arms especially. I found it inordinately fatiguing controlling the piebald and the bayard through all that frenetic uproar and crisis.

Mistrusting the atmosphere, I leaned against the side of the chariot, bent on recuperating as rapidly as possible. To husband my energy and that too of the horses was small wisdom, since who knew but what we might need it before snugly back in Carthage. Wellnear in a reverie for a time—I snapped to at one point.

To my gathering unease a military chariot-cade came by Tunisbound. This bechanced just as we were on the verge of transpiercing the farm belt at the outskirts of town. The caravan boasted some score of vehicles and the drivers were well-armed.

Discreetly, I guided the chariot off the road to let them pass. From their collective expression, I adduced the men regarded me more in disbelief than suspicion, particularly in light of the fact at that precise moment Carthaginians could have had no inkling of the Roman declaration of war. In due course, we resumed the trail. We were not, however, to be granted much more time for resuscitation.

Suddenly, I encompassed the fact there was conspicuous the presence of a veritable dust bowl on our tail but fairly well back. If the dust cloud was any yardstick, this perforce would be the chariot-cade that had just passed coming back in great haste. What prompted this turnabout? Could the Numidian laborers in some way have enkindled their suspicions about me? Just take the elementary matter of malice prepense, for one. Surely it was lucid beyond challenge, the ruffians came off second best in that scuffle?

Yet out of malevolence—since they were the culprits, not I— they could have lodged a complaint with the constabulary.

In any case, I was in no wise minded to let them overtake us to gain the reason for this sudden change.

Just then an arrow swished into the upper woodwork of the chariot itself! That woody sounding "pong" sang all too eloquently of inimical proximity. I required no further signals. I galvanzied into action!

Once anew I was reduced to the use of my whip—which by now I hated to have to wield. With an afflatus of energy the steeds surged up to a full-blown gallop.

A frantic stampede of chariots—with mine out in front by only a few hundred feet—took place. In the wake of the mad dash clouds of dust arose. Miraculously, I did better than hold my own. To all seeming, I had made an appreciable gain on my adversaries.

I could only account for this by observing the military chariots were all burdened with considerable weaponry, and each vehicle undeviatingly displayed weighty bronze insignia mortised to its sides. Approaching the great city gates, so invitingly set with their august fixed arches, I had adequate time to break speed and so pass through the portals with an air of insouciance, which I some-how managed to summon.

Holding to this inconspicuous tone, we left the area and vanished into a side street. From a secluded locale I shortly could hear the rumble of a caravan breaking in on the Great Plaza with much noisy pomp and circumstance.

Chapter XVI

Stepping into a dwarfed side street, one to lead into the grand Plaza at a position front-a-front the main city gates, I spotted a patrol heading my way. Quickly entering a shop by a side orifice, I strolled out the main entrance only to emerge onto a busy street. Dodging chariots, I soon turned into a throughway that led directly into the Plaza. Before I had reached it I could tell it was pulsating with excitement—given the hour of day, indubitably a by-product of the Baalim festival.

In the center of the great square was a statue of Hamilcar Barca. Circumvallating it was a troupe of musicians who worked their earthy things—harp, flute, and timbrel—touching off along the ramparts a bell-like refrain of tintinnabulation, as accompanied by chanting priests and vestals, the procession slowly promenaded across the square. Hither, thither and yon, conspicuous by their presence, were beggar (my, how times have changed), street vendor, sorcerer, alchemist, militiaman, sailor and civilian. The panoramic scene thus appeared an unfulfilled embodiment of something this and something that. A motley of activity so aliquant would scarcely be able to sustain much more than a momentary escape from human problems. That was, of course my quick appraisal of the ongoings.

Now, those two great gates, hopefully my passport to survival, loomed up awesomely before me. My relief that they remained open, however, was mitigated by the presence of a detail of guards! By contrast, when I had made my country excursion in the morning the gates had been very indifferently guarded.

An imposing row of commercial establishments, functioning perhaps as Carthage's great bazaar, composed the facade vis-a-vis the great wall. These tradespeople, for the most part, were ceasing business for the day. In their midst, to the contrary, was a boisterous, busy emporium, doing most manifestly a land office business. Doubtless an occurrence of the festive hour.

In my brief sojourn in town, I had become aware of the presence of some racial tension between Carthaginian and the more provincial folk, especially the Numidian resident. This was evident despite the fact that all Numidia was part of the Carthaginian empire.

In light of what was taking place in the libation garden, a thought crossed my mind. Taking into account the gates were so heavily-guarded, I bethought myself that I might cause some disturbance in the Plaza. And I did not waste time pursuing the avenue of thought.

Inconspicuously fetching up a spear that had been cast aside at the base of the Barca statue, I proceeded to employ it as an innocuous walking stick and with an air of detachment made my way to the emporium.

The lounge couches of this rather extraordinarily large vaulted hall, I shortly discovered, were arranged back-to-back, but pitched toward the centrosphere where in the inner "limelight" of the building belly dancer, clown, wrestler or tumbler might perform.

With the unceremonious assistance of the oil lamps of the main hall, I also became aware that there was an alcove near the entrance which would place me in range of some of my Carthaginian friends. With the lounge couches placed back-to-back around the hall there was the fortuitous circumstance of relatively non-integrated parties sitting, also, so juxtaposed.

On one elongated couch were a number of swarthy Numidians and on the opposite an approximately identical number of Carthaginians, like the overall attendance an amalgam of sailors, civilians and provincials.

From the shelter of my alcove I stealthily raised the spear so that it was posed against the neck of one of the Numidians. With moderate force, abruptly, I jabbed it into the fleshy area. Then, forth-

104

with lowering the staff, I ducked back into the alcove.

With beady eyes the Numidian peered about him, training his attention on the Carthaginian behind him. An exchange of words ensued; and, ultimately, the protagonists fell back to the business of imbibing—almost more to honor Goddess Baalat than to assay to forget the Roman declaration of war.

After a pause, furtively emerging in a crotched position, I once again jabbed the neck of the Numidian. This time there were no qualms about ceremony! Turning in a flash—he reached for the throat of the Carthaginian, and instantly they became locked in mortal combat.

In a matter of moments the whole place burst into bedlam, and in due course struggling figures belched out into the Plaza itself. Skirting serious part in the accelerating furor, I eased out of the booze garden into the square. To my understandable satisfaction the guards at the gates deigned not to be unco-operative! Pursuant to an interim of hesitancy and mounting concern, they began to gesticulate threateningly and ejaculate oaths of disapproval of the unseemly activity.

Finally, resigning themselves to an irrepressible urge to quell what had now parlayed itself into a full-fledged riot, the guards, without warning leaving their posts, sprinted en masse across the square.

I had no time for further protocol. With an air as casual as I could muster I slipped through the city gates without further ado—until, that is, I arrived outside!

I word it this way, for even as I got through those massive stone works of this legendary walled city—I came face to face with one more of those patrols. I do not mind adding that this was my closest brush with these African friends to that moment.

There was one thing I could be assured of about Carthaginain attitudes: in this land superstition was a flagrant commodity. Thus, with conditions just now so crisis-ridden, there could be no absolute diagnosis as to what might be the fate of some benighted captive, caught not just on the very day of the Roman proclamation in town, but during an unquelled disturbance he himself might be charged with fomenting. The coincidence of it all left the imagination at bay! Getting a gammon, automatically, for the winner. For the loser the gantlet, anything from suffocation, *par exemple,* to suffering the pleasures of Melkarth the fire god . . .

Waxing pensive in that brief moment, I focused on their headgear in particular. It was distinct by virtue of its martial emblem. This no doubt signified a regular army unit instead of one of the constabulary. In a customary sort of way, the thought crossed my mind. Everyone in Africa, even the military, wore a headgear; logical enough—the noon day sun! And I did not mind admitting it had been as hot all day as . . . well, Virgil would most eloquently be qualified to furnish the words in Latin.

But this was scarcely a ripe time for cogitations on Carthaginian headgear . . . even though mine, like my toga, was all but drenched.

In an assumed spirit of detached gaiety to accommodate the Baalim festival, I attempted with words more Greek than Phoenician to put the commander of the patrol at his ease. It was not lost on me I had that continuing communication barrier. Some supplemental effort thus became obligatory—and the sooner the better!

At once I fell to pointing at the city gateway, mounting quite vociferously a goodly bit of gibberish . . . affecting the while an expression as alarmist as possible.

By this time the effect of the din in the Plaza could distinctly be heard beyond the gates. The commander stood fascinated for a moment, but irresolute. Cognizant as to how desperate my situation was, I barked out a few words at random—at the same time waving the patrol on to the gates. Meanwhile, guilefully, I began to ease away from the body of men.

Finally, the commander opted for dispatching a small detail of soldiers to investigate the Plaza ongoings. This hiatus was my last chance.

In retrospect, I was thoroughly thankful I had not "changed my shoes" when I arrived the port of Carthage. To be sure, to switch to Punic sandals would have been unworkable anyway. There was doubtless not a pair in the whole city-state that would have fitted me. My garments, while uncomfortable and gawky enough, were tolerable—but imagine sprinting down Carthaginian streets in a pair of blister-begetting crude antelope-hide sandals! My shoes, my wondrous shoes were mercurial . . .

Chapter XVII

Without warning, leaping into action, I dashed lickety-split down the hill. My *tour de force* caught the commander flat-footed. But I quickly could tell he had not quite done with me! There was a chorus of warning shouts, for instance. I was grateful they were not followed by air-borne missiles, which may have been owing to my moving out of range so rapidly.

Rushing through a decrepit apple orchard, my chest heaving as though for dear breath, I took shelter amid the more scraggly bushes and ferns that occupied so copiously the approaches to the harbor. From almost the moment this brief haven was established, menacing guardsmen traipsed by.

Moreover, as my crowning malheur, in the course of my precipitous flight downhill, I had dropped the scimitar. Veritably, it seemed, I had acquired a talent for the obstacle race!

Fatigue was beginning to interpolate itself into the proceedings; I felt as though I was in a sudatorium, so vigorously was I perspiring.

Time and the hour of day were now to me in a state of ambivalence. The deepening shadows of evening were on my side but time itself could run out. While I had secured my position for the nonce, it proved a costly victory as things worked out. Not merely was I off the main artery to the harbor, but I had veered precariously off course. I decided the best avenue to getting squared away was to take a short cut. This I soon was to regret. The pattern common to most classical cities was that, in addition to a vortex of farmlands, grasslands and so forth (radiating out, save for the harbor area when littoral, which most of them were) the radically impoverished parts of town were outside the walled city itself.

Such the Slough of Despond where second class citizen paramountly dwelled—squatters of ill-repute, expatriates, hangers-on, ex-slaves, highway robbers, thugs, and, betimes, even pirates. All the riffraff but the ostracized beggar class, which unfortunates passed all their hours up in the city proper. During periods of war or when a town stood siege this wretched offscouring of the community, often finding itself uprooted, took refuge inside the walls. For the penurious outsiders this was no inordinate sacrifice, since their domain had only been "shanty-town," classical-style.

In the course of my self-disciplined redirecting I penetrated, for the first time in the day, what almost instinctively I could dub a *classical age* slum! The entire locale was utterly beyond description. The squalor, the filth, the fantastically primitive ways and, last but not least, the effluvium, which engendered an atmosphere I found so noxious—all but beggared the imagination. The experience added up to a sort of stultifying shock treatment. Yet I had to remain on the alert—in this accursed place above all—for the open thievery and propension to commit mayhem on innocent wayfarer just for violence's sake—without delving into the xenophobian spirit universally to prevail in the typical slum.

I found myself an *instant* target—even a couple of their wellfanged (and probably hungry) dogs proved ornery enough. I warded these off with a staff I had acquired.

I kept to a good pace, as I wended my way through incredible amounts of rat and insect infested rubbish—quite frantically hoping to get this particular show behind me *le tout sont possible!* But I shortly discovered, to my dismay, I was being followed. What had commenced as a desultory group of the curious soon augmented itself into a frightening crowd. I quickened my pace some—and shortly broke into an outright run.

Helped by the shadows of dusk, I held my own until I abruptly ingressed into a woebegone orchard—one that appeared inhabited only by inhospitable reptiles. Soon, thereafter, I regained the main road. But I was cognizant of the fact, even though now clear of shanty town, I had not completely shaken my friends, although managing, somehow, to outpace them. A few minutes later—panting like mad—I spotted a patrol further up the road, also heading for the harbor. The commander—it seemed—issued me a warning shout, which I summarily ignored. Strange to say, my various tormentors seemed on a collision course!

The mob from shanty town soon drew abreast of this very patrol, and, without much ado, a free-for-all got under way. This, as it turned out, was the denouement of my immediate predicament. For that I was thankful. From my tenuous standpoint, the community was rapidly becoming almost the incarnation of difficult surprises. How many more?

Scarcely had I reached the quayside of the harbor than I became an unwilling party to another one of these confrontations. Alas, I supposed it was all owing to my failure to register sanguinously enough on the fact a state of war existed between Rome and Carthage! This was obviously the *sanctum sanctorum* as to why the confusions so rampantly diffused themselves throughout the town.

At last satisfied I had no pursuers to interdict my headway, I made tracks for the outer piers in the northeast part of the harbor— where the waiting red-sailed bark was moored.

Fairly relaxed over the encouraging turn of events, I strode abruptly out onto the wharf. In part my haste articulated anxiety over the meeting time. In view of the *state of war* it was now most mandatory the bark quit Carthage that very evening.

Even as I gained the water's edge, forthwith, I blundered foursquare onto a full-force patrol! I had been so naive as to forget the overwhelming security climate: this ancient bastion—queen city of Carthage—was now on a war footing. And that meant martial law.

With not a moment to lose I turned and fled, optimistically into advancing night. Immediately a number of patrolmen coalesced and gave chase. I boarded, on the dead run, a galley moored nearby. Then, armed with but Hobson's choice, I proceeded to hedge-hop from boat to boat. Truly, my everlasting gratitude went out to dear goddess Baalat. In the earlier part of the day the slaves had been returned to their barracks and the crews had all gone up into the walled town to celebrate the occasion!

As I had learned at first hand in the morning, the aroma to emanate from the galley ships was rather objectionable, notwithstanding the boats were fashioned from fine fragrant cedar trees— a furtherance of the Tyric tradition, to be exact.

The unhappy condition obtained from the circumstance the galley slaves had to be enchained at their seats over prolonged periods of time. However, like incipient hygiene for the age as a whole, some elementary sanitary measures were observed. The principle behind the efforts was, belike, more materialist than humanitarian, which—given the times—proved nothing. At such times as the ships idled in port, a harbor crew swathed them most thoroughly with salt water, thereby attenuating the unpleasantness. But I had more urgent matters to engage my attention than air pollution.

For a brief time my stratagem purported to be fruitful. But this, sadly to report, turned out only the start! In spite of the drawbacks of my toga, more and more an infernal nuisance as the hours wore on, and the—happily evanescent—gastric discomfiture, to say nothing of my debilitating sudation, I had so far managed to be fleet enough to avoid capture, with all that that implied. But the sheer numbers of my adversaries were threatening to turn the scales against me.

This was dramatically the quintessence of my plight: the increscent proximity of what seemed like both reinforced patrols and *more* patrols. I was beginning to imagine that along the waterfront they were all but ubiquitous! The cloak of darkness was the saving grace. It reduced their efforts somewhat to cross purposes, partially neutralizing their advantage. Goaded on by what had become almost unadorned desperation, I leapt onto a deserted galley, one moored alongside a fellow near a wharf. Almost by intuition I became cognizant of the fact there had insidiously been developing an avant garde danger from the posse presently closing in.

Chapter XVIII

My luck, in a word, appeared to be running out. Either I faced up to them in confrontation or continued these futile efforts to flee. In nothing shy of a cold sweat, I opted to make a stand of it, selecting my perch aboard one particular galley.

As a helpful little benison, at least—having already entered upon the arena of violence—and beyond my *wildest* dreams—I found the resumption of the inexpiable activities less onerous!

How strangely events had contracted themselves into raw courage of desperado with *me* the ingenuous benign fugitive forced to submit to their *tender mercies*—unable to explain, in no position to communicate—if caught!

Crouching there in the darkness, I had not long to wait. Soon a figure loomed up over the gunwale 35 of the galley. With a sudden grappling effort I bounced the fellow into the drink. Forthwith resuming my crouching posture, I repeated the process four or five times.

This tactic proved effective until, suddenly, two adversaries appeared simultaneously! In desperation, I seized them piecemeal and succeeded in cracking their heads together. This momentarily stunning them, I eased them over the ship's side. Having made what propitiously looked to be a shambles of the avant-garde, I resumed my flight. This consisted of a hedge-hopping effort in which I resumed the pattern of progressing from ship to ship, eschewing the more exposed quayside as much as possible.

At length, I began to think I had reached the end of the long march. But that turned out a presumptious notion. Coming to the last galley alongside the pier, I leapt aboard, persuaded the *genius loci* would not ultimately abandon me.

To my consternation, I found the ship manned by some half-score of sentinels! Apparently, *already* a good part of the harbor had been cordonned off. I simply had *no* chance to retreat from this one, even though for the moment the guards seemed about as surprised as I.

In a sort of gut-desperation act I fetched up an oar and, with one blow, sent two of the critters overboard; a third, meantime, had lunged toward me with his weapon targeting in. Following on an evasive step—another swing of the oar knocked him senseless.

At this precise moment three more sentinels, brandishing some kind of weaponry, rushed me headlong!

I suddenly registered on the fact the emerging close contact aboard the boat made my oar extremely unwieldy. In the confusion, one of the men jabbed at me with some sort of spear, and forthwith I felt a stinging sensation in my left side—luckily a glancing gash no more, I later found out.

With an indifferently-well aimed blow to the jaw I slammed the fellow to the deck. Then, while grappling with another of the guards, a third one leapt on my back. Catching him by the legs I quickly wrenched him free and managed to hurl him bodily at the other guard—the impact of which sent them both sprawling to the deck.

Yet, at the bow, I discerned two more sentinels! Ostensively, the light being poor at this point, they sported sword and dagger. Grabbing up a second oar, I brought it down hopefully on a *coup de grâce* basis. In any case, the twain sort of slithered over the bowside of the galley. And that seemed to be that. But the bag of surprises in store for me was not yet expended.

Bone weary, drenched from head to toe but game, if only from reckless determination, I jumped onto the quay and, prepared for the worst, firmly gripped the oar.

And, faster than one could say Jack Robinson, I encountered yet *more* of my friends! With goodly swings I silenced three or four of them. Finally, aided and abetted by oncoming darkness, I had them at bay to a point where I could head up toward my vessel, so soon to quit the port.

It was pellucid beyond words, however, that I had bought just enough time—no more. Already torches were finding their way down into the harbor area. And this could have been a fatal development; armed with these pitch-fed lamps, as sure as shooting, they would have been able to ferret me out. This could but spell out capture and the implacable fate to follow . . .

At long last, having out-Machiavellized the horde, I gained the northeast quay-side of the harbor; and winded and unutterably weary, I drew near the red-sailed bark.

A moment or two later, seemingly exanimated to a point where any exertion was agony, I fell prostrate on the deck. The prolonged delays affecting my return to ship, were in some measure pejorative as to the success of departure itself! No sooner had the bark, with me sequestered snugly aboard, eased out into the harbor in the balm of a vigorous breeze than it was visited upon by a thousand arrows from a "phalanx" of frustrated Carthaginians, who, thanks to their goddess, were in no position to give chase. Their Parthian shot, nonetheless, was still moderately spectacular. It culminated with an exiguous batch of fire-tipped arrows zeroing in on the ship. Two or three of them set fires aboard, which the crew summarily extinguished. After that we were out of range and rid of our friends for good . . .

From my fatigue-induced delirium, I lolled away into reverie. During my brief stay in Carthage many were the sentiments to be elicited, almost as numerous as those the elders had succumbed to in the Sanhedrin. For my unwitting implication in them, I could hardly countenance with insouciance, let alone contrive with relish or imperturbation, a Lorenzo-like sweet nothing to a Jessica—

> In such a night
> Stood Dido with a willow in her hand
> Upon the wild sea-banks, and waft her love
> To come again to Carthage. **36**

The character of my departure would not remotely claim the melancholy of withdrawing Aeneas. For me, with a specific acquaintanceship with this town permanently etched upon my mind, it was an occasion for *fondest* farewell. I hasten to add it was the "gulf-of-time" gap rather than infectious alienation that churned up the inhospitality to put me in a cleft stick.

No *Plato's Republic* this city-state—yet plainly an almost atypical community at that. Different from Syracuse, different from Rome, different from Attica, different from the Peloponnesus; more like Tyre, Sidon or even Troy. Egregiously oriented toward commerce and exploration, Carthage fulfilled the Phoenician dream. She was their most flourishing colony. And while subject to the theocratic overtones of Eastern motherhood, she developed newfangled lines of aristocratic pre-eminency and, for princely merchants, materialism. While these mutations bespoke a far greater inequality of condition than that to emerge with modern society, the simplicity of the social order was in an eerie sort of way a refreshing experience . . . although I could not avouch that I found it that way *today*.

Though Carthage, like every classical city, was virtually devoid of industrial pollution, for the lineaments of primitivity of the times she remained subject to the *constant* threats of famine, drought and pestilence. While such condition of things might rebuff the wit of "environmentalist," it could hardly mitigate the almost inexorable dangers from abroad.

In spite of my cavalier treatment at the hands of Carthage, the magnitude of the predicament to haunt this community left me fascinated from the word go. The defection of Utica and resultant loss of African solidarity—bode not well for her future. But this was no insurmountable setback—providing she continued her dedicated wooing of Syracuse with an eye to severing her from the Roman allegiance. Only with Syracuse withdrawn, could Rome be reduced. But this would have to be a decision that *only* Carthage could make, with or without the help of the invidious Uticans, capped off by their magistrate *the tall one*.

But with Carthage incapable of composing her differences on the *home* front, with a vociferous minority of elders, from the very rostrum of the Sanhedrin, dividing the state most schizophrenically, burdening it with internal upheaval . . . such singleness of purpose did not seem destined to obtain for Carthage. *In actu,* was not this fabled city of antiquity placing her future in jeopardy, then and there? As for Syracuse, what superior way to impress her than Carthaginian victories over the Italian? Was not Rome now herself a full-blown rival of Syracuse *even* in Sicily?

In terms of Carthage herself, it would have required that sort of dedication to support to the full her great field commander Hannibal. And it would have presupposed the sort of unity at home to sustain such a grand design. Beyond everything, it would have insured this "twilight city" a lasting place in time . . . and, analogice, in the great Western Mediterranean struggle for supremacy . . . so importunately in the offing at that predefined moment in time.

I close this portfolio of things antiquate with this thought: notwithstanding Carthage was predestined for extinction, with nary an obelisk to mark her once whereabouts, with not even a favorite son to chronicle her, a native poet to sing her glories, an historian of the township to proclaim for all time the heyday and augustness, the deathless deeds of this golden city-state of classical days— Hannibal's enduring greatness would live on; his beloved city a misty vale of oblivion, but his incisively-chiseled monument that of the greatest soldier of all time!

Is it not in this universal context that mankind sustains its legends and "fair *forever lost* Carthage" herself is redeemed, as we trod along that huge highway of myths?

As the sailors of Tyre put their trust in the Tyrian Cynosure, as at nightfall their trim barks knifed through the somber Mediterranean waves—so Carthaginians might have vested their innermost faith in their great Hannibal, the likes of whom have not been seen since. Had they so done their destiny might have been a different one.

So, adieu from this legendary city of yore . . . this storied year TWO HUNDRED EIGHTEEN B.C.—I set my hand and seal and sail away from port of Carthage.

Cordially yours,
Andrew R. Hartfield

Postscript

Propelled along by a steady zephr, the bark cleared the outer harbor and pointed its bow on a northerly course. Thus, somewhat shy of the witching hour, this should have placed us not far from the port of Utica herself, which chanced to be those few fifteen miles to the north of Carthage.

It was merely a procedure en passant, a quirk of geography, since we had scheduled no visit to the lair of *the tall one!*

Anyway, a member of our own crew had through happenstance ingressed into the city proper only a few days previously. His description of the experience was as picturesque as it was vivid. I could only conclude that he had been blessed by his multifold deities to have gotten out of the place with all his vital organs intact!

I was attracted especially to his observations on *the tall one*. It seemed the man ruled the city-state Utica like an old-fashioned Syracusan tyrant. For even the nobles and princely merchants it was all *strictum jus,* and no nonsense!

Our sailor man, moreover, informed us that *the tall one* was not alone trying to forge a league of peoples to work *with* Rome, but seeking through intrigue, on the one hand, to broaden the suzereinty of Utica herself and, on the other, to traduce the opponents of the Hanno faction, Hannibal and the Barcine party itself, to say nothing of Carthaginian internal stability, in general.

In a word, schemery to foment disorders and even civil war in the Punic empire . . . which would vitiate its hopes to best Rome by paralyzing its intent to give complete material support to its great field commander.

A few hours of slumber having revived me, I awoke to behold a truly eerie sight. We were now in the outer bay zone, only three miles or so, off Utica, cruising along at a good pace before a brisk breeze. We were in no danger (beyond the need for nautical diligence) as the night was virtually pitch dark. But in most extravagant manner Utica, too, was engrossed in the rites honoring the goddess Baalat.

The whole town seemed to pulsate with incandescent life—aglow and agleam from a thousand lances, lighting up so graphically bits and parts of buildings and great chunks of the harbor areas. Reflecting suffusedly in the water and withal ebbing and flowing like the very water itself, it wrought a painting of the most awesome beauty. And, aware that this was the home town of *the tall one,* the forbidding moods that the irridescent sheen evoked became only the more cogent. I sat there by the gunwale transfixed as I witnessed this scene of beauty so ineffable and, at that moment in time, so irrevealed.

But it was a preterient experience for myself and crew out in our trim bark. Very soon, it became more intertwined in awayness—more elusive—evanescent—fading, fading away . . . and, even as the moments, the hours, the days flowed by . . . almost as though the barbarous illuminations of Utica functioned as a sort of catalysis for departure, I was constrained ere long to enucleate my fondest farewell to 218 B.C. and this mist-shrouded era of the distant past.

This hereby concludes one more of my adventuresome little travels to faraway lands of the bygone.

A.R.H.

Epilogue

If the author of this sparing conflation tends, to all seeming, to denigrate the late *Le Grand Charles* to a point in fancy's flowering pronounced as insupportable—he will plead his case without *ad hominem* argumentation, and, on the assumption that must wind up in a cul de sac, he will have recourse to the *impossible-to-disengage* realities of the situation. *Ma foi*—yes!

A catalogue raisonné of mistakes made and verities quashed—a veritable documentary of ill-starred deeds, madcap superciliousness and studied foppish grandeur that whether Parisian or Marseillais-style might only ampliate a commerce of knaves, would-be dictators or egregious fools.

So, in some preposterous sort of way, these annotations could but bear out the princeps *res ipsa loquitur*. Beyond the *Free French*, which collapsed into outright obstructionism, what was there to remain but a balloon-size windbag? With Algiers a sellout and Dien bien phu a surrender 37 and la belle France, a simpering improvident propitiation of the *enemy,* the de Gaullian years were as a Boeotian "mastery" *de haut en bas!*

The skeptical shopper in any market place, any place, is most likely to shop around a bit. By this token, where his society is an open one, he will inherently strive to give his support to what he regards the best leadership in his own country, if not the world.

He might thence commence, diligently, to jot down a nomenclature of his own preferences.

But on second thought—why compose a list at all? One so elongated as to arouse tedium. Or is it the other way around: to compile a list at all would prove so arduous a project as to be counterproductive? Let the issue, then, be equitably resolved on the strength of a mere question or two.

Who really needed the luxury of *that tall fellow?* Who so late reigned, almost like Charles the Sixth, in this city on the Seine, whose personal power-lust transformed the very constitution of France herself? Could a figure of such destructive bent stand with the giants of the entire body of time *a posteriori* the Age of Metternich, the American Revolution, the Age of Enlightenment, the European Renaissance or Fifth and Fourth centuries B.C. Greece?

END

H-B-SARGENT

Footnotes

1. In the Nineteenth century, after fending off the threat of Napoleon, a degree of co-existence with the West prevailed for a time with the Holy Alliance and other accords pursuant to the resettlement of European boundaries and the Congress of Vienna of 1815. Subsequently, Russia, with no place to go in the West, resumed her Eastern and Southern expansion; and while seeking to pacify the Caucasus became embroiled in wars with the Avars; and, subsequently, in the Crimean War and in new wars with Turkey, now become "the sick man" of Europe. The latter confrontations concerned "the Eastern (or, more narrowly, Black Sea) Question": the rise of Russia as a European power from the Eighteenth century and its expansion to the south at the expense of a decaying Ottoman empire.
Beyond this, vis-a-vis European powers, Russia in addition to a diplomatic setback at the Congress of Berlin of 1878 and a confrontation with the Poles (Russian Poland) manifested concern about Prussian expansion and British influence in the Middle East.
2. In this unceasing determination, of course, Soviet expansion is aided and abetted by super weaponry and outer space machines, a vast military establishment, global politico-economical warfare, the exporting of terror (together with the training of terrorists both in the Soviet Empire and elsewhere) in conjunction with a furthering of "national liberation" movements in both the Third and Free Worlds and, finally, a massive international espionage apparatus under the aegis of the Soviet internal-security and intelligence vehicles—namely, the K.G.B. (Committee for State Security) and the G.R.U. (Soviet Military Intelligence). In today's world the Soviet Union's role, shaped by history and a severe environment, is that of the "Mars of malcontents." Already proprietress of a vast empire reaching from the Pacific Ocean to the three Baltic states, Latvia, Lithuania and Esthonia—she too is a power that asserts effectual hegemony over most of the Balkan states and those of Eastern Europe, including Poland, which territorial areas she has long regarded as her own private preserve. Since World War II only the geopolitical defeats in Austria and Egypt (and the Mexican standoff with

Finland, as an outcome of the Winter War of 1939–40) and the defection of strategically-placed Yugoslavia under Tito have stood out as bastions of restraint against this relentless Soviet expansion—a diastole that clearly broke the Monroe Doctrine with the conversion of Cuba into a Russian satellite. The Western World is presently in an era in which we witness the phenomenon of society levelling off at lowest common denominators, with respect to both equality of condition and the cultural state; engineered on the thrust of accelerating technology enhancing unduly a wayward population growth, whose quintain becomes apotheosis of the demos and the atrophy of the socius, and catalyzing the circumstances of society returning to its *natural* state after an artificial eon (namely, the Great European Frontier Age, c. 1350—c. 1910 A.D.). By way of testimonial, observe the breakdown in social morals, the relentless exacerbating of the crime rate in all sectors of society, such empiricism cast in the crucible of spiritual decay and begetting of parallel forces of socioeconomic erosion, whose most dramatic lucubrations are inexorable inflation and confiscatory taxation—hence, fiscal decay and ultimate social ruin. In short, Twentieth century society—the urban community of the industrial world—having rid itself of the time-honored city walls, finds itself returned to a walled state of Medieval anarchy, with terror-fecundating crime and conjugate derring-do widespread and the *external* barbarians at the gates. Thus, notwithstanding the soft spots around the globe that the Russian Empire would seek to commandeer and eventually annex—to wit, Latin America, central Africa, southeast Asia and the Persian Gulf area—the civilized world has its own protracted malaise with which it must come to grips. Yet the profluent Polish unrest, as an assault on the idiosyncratic apocrypha of Marxist socialism, beyond representing heresy, serves as an acute reminder that the obsolete Russian Empire itself is long past due for dismantling. This would seem history's verdict—no matter how such sustained contraction might induce that other superpower Mainland China to pretergress her current geopolitical role. Moreover, the intensification of thermonuclear weapons and the workable equipment to accommodate it, together with the ramified sophistication in wielding the techniques of war, both in outer space and on earth, are bound through acculturation to expose even the Third World to the ultra-advanced technology. While the understandable rivalry between two diametrically opposed systems seems unavoidable over a protracted period of time, the spread of modern weaponry may turn out as great a worriment over world stability. Still and all, for a prolonged interim of time in the rivalry of Warsaw Pack countries under the Soviet suzerainty and the NATO powers led by the United States, the notion of a polite cessation of militarism mutually endorsed, in the light of a naive concept, such as Mutual Assured Destruction (MAD), must be tabled in favor of outright endorsement of the precept that a desperate Soviet Union is determined enough to win the world by hook, crook, holocaust or blackmail—no matter what SALT II or non-SALT II treaties are supposed to designate. In short, a "Soviet war-winning doctrine" supercedes all else, whether the trappings of an epoch of alleged détente or a time of concrete international covenants.

 3. The chief periods of Russian history—

   1) The period of Independent Principalities—commencing with the founding kings of Novgorod (862–1237)

   2) The Mongol or Tartar Domination (1238–1462) (The Golden Horde invasion 1237–40)

3) The Tzardom of Muscovy (1462–1584)
4) The "modern" empire
   —(transitional) (1584–1613)
   —House of Romanov (1613–1917)
   (Michael Romanov) (1613–45)
5) The Bolshevik dictatorship under Lenin (1917–24) (from the Russian revolution of 1917 to the death of Lenin)
6) The Stalinist autocracy (1924–1953)
7) The ongoing oligarchy (now also a gerontocracy) 1953—

In the scale of time the world is presently in the *post*-Great European Frontier Age (c. 1350–c. 1910); with the *external* barbarians of the modern world (following upon the aborted challenges of *internal* Nazi Germany (and Fascist Italy) and *external* Japan) the Russian Empire (the so-called Soviet Union) together with client nations and the (until recently) mainland or communist Chinese, who for their approximately 4,500 mile territorial contiguity with the menacing Russian Empire are metamorphosing out of the role of *external* barbarian—thus, converting the world geopolitical stage into a quaternary one: the Free World (the West), the Russian Empire, mainland China and the Third World. The easement on the part of the Chinese vis-a-vis the Russians was also due to some notable historical developments that prevented the *very* valid *domino theory* from becoming practical in Southeast Asia and elsewhere—such as General Suharto, now president of his country, saving Indonesia from communism and—yes—the Vietnam War (and before it the Korean War)—which events together bought the vitally-needed time to destroy the already teetering alliance between mainland China and the Soviet Union, alike to vitiate the effectiveness of overseas communist Chinese expansion. Further, the saving of Indonesia from communism amounted to a constraint on the Soviet Union's policy that forced her into a passive role. After all, Indonesia is predominantly a Moslem land, and dwelling inside the Russian Empire are tens of millions of Moslems. In short, these East Asian developments ipso facto helped to end the threat of World domination by the *external barbarians* of the modern world—under siege to which, shortly after World War II, the Free World had been (e.g., The Cold War, The Iron Curtain, The Bamboo Curtain). Overall, the world, from the human standpoint kaleidoscopic and unfathomable, might be likened to a constancy in fluxion, thus a fixed body subject to ceaseless change, applying to the industrial nations as well as the Third World. Yet, despite the myriad matters to exercise contemporary man, there is little question about the purport of the libretto of the Soviet Union just now: this anachronistic empire constitutes far and away the greatest disturbance to world equilibrium in these turbulent times.

However, economic and fiscal challenges by Japan and the Arab world (the one energy poor, the other too energy rich) to occupy in a geopolitical way a piece of the present world stage constitute potentially insidious realities, alike a possible presence therein of the concurrently enigmatic mainland Chinese.

4. By maintaining an army in Spain the eventual victor over Hannibal at Zama (202 B.C.) denied his rival the supplies and seige equipment he needed to take Rome. This sustained interjection was only the more calamitous in the light of Caius Claudius Nero's victory over Hannibal's brother Hasdrubal in the battle of the Metaurus (207 B.C.).

5. The Scientific Method, cornerstone of modern science.

6. Whose vis-a-vis are perspicacity and systematic thought.

7. However, for the ego-ditheistic nature of man, delineating two visceral forces, one good the other evil, the paramountcy of the matter must remain not a sexuality content so much as a blind irrational will. But modern psychoanalysis depends on the notion of "dogma eat dogma." Yet even sillier than Sigmund Freud is Karl Marx. We have before us various models around the world to tell us how fared the application of his notions of *scientific socialism*.
Quite so!

In the Soviet Union, for instance, Marxism (even if remolded by that old fake Lenin) gives us not a "workers paradise" but a "workers hell." In many lands of Africa and Asia the so-called revolutionary uplift of the workers is to be equated with rule by ochlocrats—usually, when not an outright military dictatorship, goons, thugs or pistol-packing rapists. One could be instantly minded to think of Fidel Castro of Cuba or that erstwhile butcher—Tito. Marx, it will be argued, being himself a European was not thinking of Russia and other parts of the world, with the exception of Europe-oriented North America. He had in mind the industrialized European countries in particular for the application of his theses of sociopolitical revolution. But—a big but—Europe had revolutions—not just rebellions—and had them aplenty across the years—three relatively modern ones giving us Hitler, Mussolini and Franco and their "governments of the people to a fault." Even the French communes, variously from the Hundred Years War to the last wicked one—that of Paris in 1871—were hardly picnic outings to watch the U.S. Civil War's "The First Battle of Bull Run!" Of all these delusory Nineteenth century innovators the only one worth a pig's haunches is Charles Darwin. But even this chap has been quite harshly smitten these days by the "creation vs evolution" dilemma.
Still and all, Darwin was enlightening; and at least he was not mentally ill, like Freud, or mad, like Marx.

8. One of the suffetes (Sofetim) or chief magistrates elected annually (of which there were two).

9. The Second *Punic War* (sometimes "Hannibalic War") (218–201 B.C.).

10. Baalat or Baalath (but not to be confused with the Paphian goddess Aphrodite).

11. The First *Punic War* (268 or 264–241 B.C.).

12. Cartagena or Carthagena—Latin *Carthago Nova* "new Carthage" (seaport of south-eastern Spain) was founded by Hasdrubal Pulcher (brother-in-law of Hannibal) about the year 243 B.C., according to *Encyclopaedia Britannica;* about the year 225 B.C., according to The Columbia Encyclopedia. It was identified as *Carthago Nova* or New Carthage, so as not to confuse it with the African city of Carthage, a measure of its importance almost from its very founding. Noted for its fabled silver and gold mines, it became the urban headquarters and treasury of the Punic army.
When Scipio Africanus Major took the city in 209 B.C. it was more than the loss of a source of great wealth to Carthage. It spelled the collapse of the Carthaginian Spanish empire, with Hannibal's forces in Italy effectually cut off from home.

13. Ancient name *Melissa*.

14. According to the 11th edition of *Encyclopaedia Britannica,* Carthage espoused the use of the elephant in war in the Third century B.C., thus emulating the kings of Syria and Egypt. Moreover, also according to this source, the elephant

employed was the African type *(elephas capensis)* more diminutive than the Asiatic *(elephas indicus)* but with longer ears. The second edition of The Columbia Encyclopedia alludes to the SE Asia and Indian elephant as *elaphas*. The latter source also makes note of the large African elephant *(loxodonta)*, now located only south of the Sahara. It is possible *Encyclopaedia Britannica* was referring to the pygmy elephant of W. Africa.

15. Hamilcar Barca. Hannibal actually had two (known) brothers, both generals—Hasdrubal and Mago. Their brother-in-law Hasdrubal Pulcher succeeded to the command in Spain upon the death of his father-in-law (Hamilcar Barca), who fell sword in hand during a battle with the natives. Following the assassination of Hasdrubal in 221 B.C. Hannibal assumed command in Spain. Some three years after taking charge war broke out (the Second *Punic War*), so Hannibal deputed, in turn, the command to his next younger brother Hasdrubal when he himself launched his Italian campaign.

16. Naval battle of the First *Punic War*—Aegates or Aegusae (Aegadian Isles) 241 B.C. After this naval defeat Carthage sued for peace. Other naval battles of note: Mylae 260 B.C. and Ecomus 256 B.C. (both lost by Carthage) . . . the latter described by H. G. Wells in *The Outline of History* as "probably the greatest naval engagement of antiquity 700–800 big ships engaged."

The Romans, while newcomers to the naval world, apparently relied upon Greek navigational experience and personnel (apart from galley slaves) to achieve supremacy through, in part, the development of more sophisticated "naval architecture."

Ecnomus undoubtedly included a number of a new type of "battleship—quinqueremes (galleys with five banks of oars on both sides). The standard size until perhaps Mylae was the trireme, which featured out three rows of oars." (A ship with four banks of oars was known as a quadrireme.)

Doubtlessly, at the naval battle of Ecnomus the Romans employed their crafty innovation the *Corvus* . This was "a sort of long draw-bridge on their ships, held up to a mast by a pulley and with grappling hooks and spikes at the end. They also loaded their galleys with soldiers. Then as the Carthaginian rammed or swept alongside, this *Corvus,* as it was called, could be let down and the boarders could swarm aboard him."

"Instead of relying upon ramming or breaking the oars of the adversary, which demanded more seamanship than they possessed, they" looked for a way "to board the enemy" with soldiery—which put another way meant a means for exporting their militarism, which had been so successful on terra firma.

17. Modern name Messina; ancient names Zancle and the above.

18. In Roman legend—Dido.

19. Conspicuous by their absence were some nameless leaders that had "fallen into disfavor"—Malchus, a certain Fourth century Hanno of the Barcide house, one Bomilcar and so on.

20. Melkarth or Melkart (Moloch "the abomination of the Ammonites" deemed to be Milcom) was actually the Baal of Tyre. Moloch, variously Molech, Malcham or Milcom, was the Canaanitish god of fire.

21. "Carthage must be destroyed." According to recorded history, there was at least one Roman senator who was not so purblind: as a sort of parody of Cato's unrelenting *delenda est Carthago* he employed at the close of every speech the peroration "Carthage must stand."

This was Scipio Nascia; manifestly, wisdom had told him the presence and stimulus of Carthage was a contributory factor in the prosperity of Rome herself, to say nothing of civilization in general.

In a capsule, the two titans could work together to mutual advantage, rather than behave as two scorpions in a bottle. Ironically, M. Porcius Cato the Elder's grisly admonishment was an accretion to follow an official visit he made to Carthage where he was thoroughly impressed with the city.

22. Arnold Bennett.

23. Since this Hanno flourished from 250-200 it is almost a certainty he was the man who assumed a virtually adversary role in the First *Punic War,* culminating in the revolt of the mercenaries—the same antagonist in town who so fervently opposed the Hannibalic ventures in Spain and thereafter Italy.

24. If not outright pioneers in the art of road paving they appear to have been more advanced than most contemporary communities. Astley J. H. Goodwin had that to say on the subject in chapter 8 of his work *Rome of the Emperors.*

25. The Judaistic approach to religion, antedating Christianity by centuries, metamorphosed into monotheism, a departure in the spiritual order for so long to become at loggerheads with Phoenician polytheism.

The Phoenicians with their chief colonies Carthage and Utica, however, continued to adhere to the rites of their pantheistic religion. And, in effect, each city had her own special deity.

Often called, Baal, Lord or Moloch (Melkarth) the temple for each community abided as the very centerpiece of social, civil and religious life. It is believed that owing to the contiguousness of Sicilian Greeks and Carthaginians from the close of the Fourth century Hellenic religious influences began to become meaningful. A temple to Apollo was erected in the agora (forum) of Carthage. The temple featured a colossal statue, which penultimately was to wind up in Rome. Other examples of acculturation are confirmed by *votive stelae* that have been unearthed. These parallels aside, Baal-Ammon or Moloch, "the great god of all Libya," must be deemed identical with the Tyrian Melkarth or Melkart. Yet probably for the nebulosity of Phoenician designation other interpretations have had their day in court.

The 11th edition of *Encyclopaedia Britannica,* for instance, imputes to Melkarth a totally different role. According to this source, there towered over "an army of minor deities" a "trinity of great gods composed of Baal-Ammon or Moloch (identified by the Romans with Cronus or Saturn); Tanit, the virgin goddess of the heavens and the moon, the Phoenician Astarte, and known as Juno Caelestis in the Roman period; Eshmun, the protecting deity and protector of the acropolis, generally identified with Aesculapius. There were also special cults: of Iolaus or Tammuz-Adonis, whom the Romans identified to some extent with Mercury; of the god Patechus or Pygmaeus, a deformed and repulsive monster like the Egyptian Ptah, whose images were placed on the prows of ships to frighten the enemy; and lastly of the Tyrian Melkarth, whose functions were analogous to those of Hercules. The statue of this god was carried to Rome after the siege of 146 (Pliny, *Nat. Hist.* xxxvi. 12.39). From inscriptions we know the names of other minor deities, which are perhaps only other names of the same gods, e.g. Rabbat Umma, 'the great mother'; Baalat haedrat, 'mistress of the sanctuary'; Ashtoreth (Astarte), Illat, Sakon, Tsaphon, Sid, Aris (?Ares)."

Apropos of Greek influence, this source further declares that "the Carthaginians once at least sent offerings to Delphi, and Tanit approximated to some extent to

Demeter; hence on the coins we find the head of Tanit or the Punic Astarte crowned with ears of corn, in imitation of the coins of the Greek Sicilian colonies. The symbol of Tanit is the crescent moon; in her temple at Carthage was preserved a famous veil or *peplus* which was venerated as the city's palladium."

From "Carthage" in *Encyclopaedia Britannica*.
11th edition (1910–11).

26. Tyre was herself originally a colony of Sidon, which she proceeded to eclipse in prominence with the passage of time.

27. At the outset of the Second *Punic War* both Rome and Carthage were moving out of the Early Iron Age, whose chief contribution to material progress was glass. In addition to their development of the alphabet, (which was designed under the impetus of accommodating international trade), the Phoenicians are also credited with introducing the dye called Tyrian purple and inventing glass.

It is a known fact the Carthaginians were quite highly sophisticated in matters commerce and trade—and very likely banking. The business of gold and silver dealings was probably time-honored. In his book *East and West* in a chapter on Carthage and Rome, C. Northcote Parkinson pointed out in effect that Carthaginian coins reach back as early as the Fourth century B.C. The images of a palm tree and horse appear on some. In general, the head of a monster graced the prow of the ancient war galley, the diaphanous intent being to scare the enemy; but Parkinson pointed out what must have been a departure. In Tyre at some point they began bedecking the prow with a horse's head, and this custom became quite commonplace at Cadiz. Eventually, they came to be called "Hippi." These ships roamed at least as far as the African Atlantic coast. In about 112 B.C. one of the figureheads was taken to Egypt from a ship-wreck on the East African coast; the conclusion reached by experts was that it was a piece of a galley from Cadiz. Clearly the Carthaginians followed in the footsteps of the tradition of enterprise behind them. The matter of imagination, however, was something again. What has survived of their art forms, while not to be ignored, was designed more for utility than attractiveness.

28. Of course, manifold were the servile labors of the day. In addition to oarsmanship, slaves worked the mines, labored in the factories at the most lowly tasks, tilled the soil in the employ of citizen farmers, performed household duties including attending to their masters, held humble offices in connection with the temples and the courts, played a part in the execution of public works, the construction of roads, the cleansing of sewers and the maintenance of aqueducts. There were in addition to captives other areas whence slavery was alimented— such as loss of citizenship or "freemanship" as punishment for the commission of crime.

Then, in Rome especially, were those slaves known as *gladiators*. Slavery at first met limited needs (probably mostly for galley, construction and household), thereafter rampant. Serfdom evolved out of slavery during *the defensive era* in contrast to *the age of conquest*.

29. As for Rome herself, Toynbee depictured "bread and shows"—*panem et circenses* as eventuating from the Second century B.C. to the Sixth of the Christian Era.

30. The belief that entertains the widest acceptance seems to be that *Carthage* (Lat. *Carthago* or *Carchedon)*, through her Phoenician appellation *Karthadshat*, "New City," enjoyed such designation to distinguish her from her sister Tyrian

colony Utica, which meant "Old City." However, there is enough confusion surrounding the matter to attribute the name perhaps to a linguistic divagation. This theory holds that the error pertains not to differentiating between "old" and "new" towns but in the name Carthage itself. It is argued that the inhabitants themselves called their city "Kirjath-Hadeshath," which means "The New Town," "The Old Town" being either Tyre or Utica. While the Romans called the city Carthage and the Greeks Karchedon, it is deemed to be the corruption of a Canaanite word for town *Kirjath,* which may be found in such names as Kirjath-Baal and Kirjath-Jearim in Scripture.

31. When, according to tradition, Aeneas ostensibly under divine command deserted Dido she allegedly destroyed herself on her own funeral pyre. Since Aeneas had taken with him "the palladium of Carthage"—the statue Pallas Athena—the citizenry soon felt faced with a grave crisis, given the prevailing supersititons of the times: they were now without a symbol of municipal protection. In desperation, they created a new palladium for the town, and this turned out to be a veil, duly sanctified and placed in the temple of Tanit (a Semitic goddess of love related to Astarte).

32. It was in this very temple that some of the last remnants of the Punic forces resisted the soldiery of Scipio Africanus Minor (at the close of the Third *Punic War).*

33. Inasmuch as Carthage arose amid a world of Libyan tribes, from which it purchased the original site of Byrsa hill, scholars believe Carthage came to have a sizable minority Libyan population. Thus, the population of the city, estimated at around 700,000 just prior to the Third *Punic War* (149 B.C.) was partly of Phoenician and partly of Libyan descent.

34. But irrespective of this obligatory custom of sacrifice plied in specific rituals, it would appear the worship invested more energy into this sort of obeisance—together with the indulgence of the fertility rites—with the passage of time.
And the evolving into dualism to the point where, in the polytheistic pantheon concerned, Baal and Melkarth (also called Molech or Moloch "the abomination of the Ammonites"—accounted as Milcom) might wellnigh be likened to *good* and *evil*—the fertility observances and those of fire and war; for these bespoke a Melkarthian worship become widely disparate for the human sacrificial rite (superinduced for the debasing of Baalish practices—rendering the deity correspondent with Baal-zebub, "lord of the flies," and complimentary to the deity Baal).

35. Approximately, anything from the *wales* to the *sheer strakes.*

36. William Shakespeare, *The Merchant of Venice.*

37. With respect to these erstwhile French colonies—Algiers and Indo-China—and elsewhere there was an extenuating circumstance that palliated the act of abandonment of such domains by France. This was the inexorable arrival of the post-colonial period, sweeping in on the wave of two world wars, that made the relinquishment of empire by European powers inevitable.
Thus, pellucidly, de Gaulle was anxious to liquidate the Algerian War, which had long been a losing proposition. In this commerce he had company, accross the board: everywhere the erstwhile European colonial powers wanted out, but the problem that dogged the issue was how to extricate themselves from domains that had become counter-productive? The Age of Colonialism had ended and the new "age of Soviet (-Sinae) neo-colonialism" was just getting under way. It was for these circumstances that Western leaders determined to stage a rear guard action,

in such a way—in the time-honored interplay of East and West—as to debar Eastern powers, the Eastern world, from untracking too puissant an insurgency vis-a-vis a now contracting West.

But not Charles de Gaulle. His predilection from the outset was ignominious withdrawal . . . defeat at almost any price—in Africa, in Indochina, even in France's dealings with the Soviet Union (where there was no quid pro quo compact at all: far from helping to sustain a Western quarantine of Moscow, the Frenchman indulged himself in unilateral abject adulation, notwithstanding his prior denunciation of the Soviet Union some two decades earlier (from 1947)). Now, it has been argued de Gaulle gave the French people back their pride—since they had been wallowing in the Slough of Despond, where they had been ensconced for most of this century to that point in time and for upwards of half of the last. But, if so, their recovery of that pride was achieved at a gigantean price: inasmuch as it alienated France effectually from her traditional allies for an indeterminate period, thrust France into a predator role—one in which she disallowed military arrangements for Western defense respecting her soil, placed into question the European Common Market, overtly challenged the purposes of NATO and, finally, embarked on a personalized diplomacy with Germany, Russia and the Far East. The recovered pride also cajoled the French into fiscal folly, leaving their economy at the brink.

As to de Gaulle as politician his career bespoke a socioeconomic void and an ideological disaster—de Gaulle actually gave witting or unwitting succor to the French communists at every turn. His provisional government of June, 1944, lasting until Oct., 1944, remained bereft of any semblance of credence in the eyes of the principle allies. Then, after being unanimously elected provisional president of the new French Republic in Nov., 1945 (which de Gaulle himself was to denounce after it became formalized as the Fourth Republic, Dec., 1946) he abruptly resigned (Jan., 1947). Why? Simply because the very leftist parties (and roustabout-students) he had so advertently encouraged through pigheadedness, unleashing them into riotous behavior in Paris and elsewhere, now ceased to support him. And what of de Gaulle's later, second round in the presidency, a public life stint to befall well after he had headed a new coalition in 1947 (the Reunion of the French People)? More of the same, more road blocks in the path of Western defense and stability, more go-it-alone lag-bed enterprise, more flatulence, magniloquence and megalomania!

Even much of his military career, apart from his World War I service and the high water mark epoch of the *Free French,* amounted to that of trumped-up militarism, respecting not alone tactics and strategies but even military career as an officer (not attaining the rank of general until 1940 and in absentia at that).

This pattern seemed apparent especially after his capture by the Germans in World War I in 1916 and his service under Gen. Maxime Weygand in Poland in 1921.

Now, for the very nature of the World War II French upheaval (soon to be a fallen power under the heel of Nazi Germany) the basic eventualities of de Gaulle finally making it to brigadier general and the concomitant fact that in that very year he was anointed undersecretary of war under Premier Paul Reynaud, could not easily elude the underpinning of an artificial environment. In any case, de Gaulle shortly fled to London where he organized the *Free French* forces.

That development launched his only major claim to real accomplishment; while in England (which he hated so profoundly) he formed the *Free French* National Committee and, in time, the growing *Free French* forces were successful in Syria, Madagascar and North Africa.

True enough, de Gaulle did manage to write a military work—namely, *The Army of the Future* (1934). But this painstaking effort scarcely made the man a prophet. His notions of mobility in the modern army and all the adjunctive paraphernalia had been profoundly delved into by such students of tactical and strategic militarism and the concepts of total war as Antoine Henri Jomini and Karl von Clausewitz and others and—also impressively—illustrated by the military campaigns of Graf von Moltke and Alfred Garf von Schlieffen (author of the Schlieffen plan).

To sum up, by way of closing, after a somewhat short-lived meteoric military rise to fame, all turned ultimately sour once de Gaulle immersed himself in the political sphere—for the great part due to his unswerving highhandedness, nauseating superciliousness and incalcuable self-centeredness (even the U.S. State Dept. opposed him in much of these post-war activities).

For these reasons, chiefly, when on Aug. 26, 1944, the Provisional (French) Government returned to Paris, Charles de Gaulle's political accomplishments had already overreached the twilight zone.

After that, there was at hand only the spectacle of a misfit statesman playing the fool on history's stage to his heart's content. C'est-ca! The Grand Charles quietly donned the vale of Hinnom and just as quietly invited La Belle France to venture out with him at her own risk.